Owning an
Electric Car

2010 Edition

Michael Boxwell

Greenstream Publishing

D1089450

Greenstream Publishing

Greenstream Publishing
12 Poplar Grove
Ryton on Dunsmore
Warwickshire
CV8 3QE
United Kingdom

www.greenstreampublishing.com

Published by Greenstream Publishing 2010

First Edition – published February 2010
Second Edition *(Revised)* – published April 2010

ISBN 978-1-907670-01-5

A previous revision of this book was published
by Code Green Publishing under ISBN 978-1-907215-10-0

Editors: Barry Evans, Nikki Gordon-Bloomfield
Proof Readers: Adrian Procter, Angela Boxwell
Researcher: Angela Boxwell

TABLE OF CONTENTS

Foreword by Quentin Willson 1

About this book 3

    About the author.. 5

Introducing the electric car.. 7

    What is an electric car? 8

    How an electric car compares to a conventional car 8

    Is range the weakest point of an electric car?................................. 10

    Are electric cars the silent killer? 13

    Other forms of electric cars 15

    Chapter Summary... 19

Living with an electric car.. 21

    First impressions 21

    Plugging It In... 24

    The first few weeks 25

    Borrowing a 'plug full' of electricity 28

    Electric Car charging points.. 29

    Long Distance Driving 30

    Long Term Ownership 31

    Chapter Summary... 33

Will an electric car work for me? 37

    What benefits will I get from owning an electric car?..................... 37

    Where do I live and where do I drive? 38

    How far do I travel in an average day?.. 38

    Where can I plug in? 39

    Can I charge my car elsewhere? 41

    Can I remove the batteries to recharge them? 41

    How often do I need to be able to drive further than an electric car will allow me to go?.. 41

    What if an electric car is not suitable for me now? 42

    Chapter Summary... 44

Purchasing and Running Costs 45

    Leasing schemes.. 45

    Fuel Costs.. 45

    Purchasing or leasing batteries? 47

    Electric car purchasing plans... 47

    Servicing Costs.. 48

Resale Values 48
Chapter Summary 49
Electric Cars you can drive today 51
Categories of electric car 51
Electric vehicles you can buy today: 57
Aixam 60
American Electric Vehicle 61
Aptera 61
BYD 62
Citroen 62
Chevrolet India 63
Coda Automotive 64
CommuterCars 64
Dynasty 65
Effedi 65
Electric Car Corporation 66
Estrima 66
Ford 67
G-Wiz 68
GEM 68
Green Vehicles 69
Kandi 69
Kewet 69
Liberty 71
Miles 71
MINI 71
Mitsubishi 72
MyCar 73
Myers 74
Nissan 74
Peapod 75
Peugeot 76
Phoenix 76
Renault 77
REVA 79
Mercedes-Smart 80
Start Lab 81
Stevens 82
SunMotor 82
Tata 83
Tazzari 83
Tesla 84
TH!NK 84
Toyota 86
Twike 86
Venturi 87
Wheego 87

ZAP!.. 88

Electric Car Conversions.. 89
    Chapter Summary.. 91

Buying a used Electric Car... 93
    Do your research 93
    Join an owners club 94
    Where to find used electric cars for sale.................................. 95
    What to look for when buying a used electric car 95
    Getting expert advice 98
    The test drive... 98
    Servicing your used electric car 100
    Chapter Summary.. 100

Electric cars and the environment 103
    Before we begin 103
    How to create a comparison between electric cars and conventional cars ... 103
    An acknowledgement to Motor Manufacturers...................... 105
    Air Pollution.. 105
    The current view on Air Pollution from Traffic 106
    Air Pollution from Electricity Power Stations....................... 112
    How our energy is produced 114
    How gasoline, petrol and diesel are produced....................... 115
    'Well to Service Station' efficiency for car fuels 118
    Where our electricity comes from 119
    Electric Cars and Electricity Supply...................................... 128
    Fuel Economy 131
    The environmental impact of batteries 136
    The environmental impact of vehicle manufacturing and distribution........ 139
    The environmental impact of vehicle recycling 140
    Chapter Summary.. 141

Real world economy figures for electric cars.............................. 143
    The test... 143
    Test validity... 144
    The electric cars 144
    The combustion engine cars... 145
    Test results from the electric cars:... 146
    What if they were powered by coal? 146
    Test results from the combustion engine cars 147
    Side by side analysis: well to wheel measurements 148
    Side by side analysis if powered by coal................................ 148
    Chapter Summary.. 148

A final word.. 149

Appendix A: A brief history of electric cars 151
    Learning the lessons from history 155

Appendix B: Electric vehicles in business 158

Types of electric vehicle available 158
Is an electric vehicle suitable for my business? 160
Charging facilities and Commercial Vehicles 162
Electric Vehicles and employees 162
Promoting your business with Electric Vehicles 162
Electric Commercial Vehicles you can buy today 163
Chapter Summary 166
Appendix C: Electric Vehicles and Local Government 167
How local government can help the adoption of electric vehicles in their
locality 167
Do people use electric cars instead of bus services? 169
Chapter Summary 170
Appendix D: Other electric vehicles 171
Electric Bicycles 171
Electric Motorbikes and Scooters 172
Electric Commercial Vehicles 172
Electric Aircraft 172
Electric Boats 173
Chapter Summary 173
Appendix E: Free – working towards a radical price 174
Anyone want a free car? 174
The mobile phone model 175
Making the mobile phone sales model work for cars 175
Appendix F: Charging an electric car with renewable power 177
Charging up an electric car with solar 177
Solar powered cars 178
Commercially Available Solar Charging Stations 179
Finding out more about solar 180
Wind Power 180
Chapter Summary 181
Appendix H: The website 183
Want More? 184
Glossary 185
Index 187

FOREWORD BY QUENTIN WILLSON

It was an easy call. Abandon the car or get shot. Downtown Los Angeles isn't the place to break down. A score of sullen eyes watched me from the tenement rooftops as I frantically tried to restart the General Motor's EV1 prototype, but the battery was toast. Leaving a multi-million dollar vision of the future casually parked outside a burnt out apartment block felt impossibly reckless but the cops in the cruising black and white who rescued me said it was probably the best decision of my life. Such potential, so much money, so many high hopes, all lost because the battery pack expired after 17 miserable miles.

That was a decade ago. And today I'm driving another electric car, a Mitsubishi i-MiEV. A realistic battery range of 80 miles, top whack of 85 mph, four seats, four doors and a cost of just under a quid for a full charge mean that this electric car is bewitchingly usable. Ten years of development has brought a raft of electric cars onto the market and some, like the Tesla roadster, really are blindingly good. None are cheap, they still don't do long distances and we badly need a simple, easily accessible charging infrastructure, but the technology is now mainstream, works reasonably well and can only get sharper. Engineers around the world are toiling like troglodytes to crack the 300-mile Holy Grail of battery range. And it won't be long.

Electric cars may only be medium term because hydrogen power is the real deal but that's still another 20 years away. Until then electric vehicles are going to start appearing on every street. And that's because once you've driven one you'll never look back. Eerily silent, amazingly quick, they cost pennies to run and are potentially cleaner than a field full of wild flowers. Emissions from coal-fired power stations may not be ideal but most early adopters of EVs are likely to be more interested in energy security than CO_2. The price of oil is far too vulnerable to manipulation and is only

1

going to get more expensive still. And not having the constant tyranny of fifty quid fill-ups feels pretty good to me.

So if you're a town bound driver think seriously about an electric car. There are sizable government grants, parking and road tax concessions and subsidized leasing deals. You *will* run out of juice, never travel anywhere without a jumbo-sized extension cord and small crowds will gather wherever you park. But the glow of warm approval you'll feel from all that novelty and silent speed will make you smile endlessly. Ten years ago I'd never have believed just how fascinating, fun and futuristic it could be living with an electric car.

Quentin Willson

January 2010

Quentin Willson is one of the UK's best-known motoring authorities. A presenter of BBC Top Gear for 12 years, founder of Channel 5's Fifth Gear and regular face on BBC News, ITV's Tonight and GMTV. He's also won Motoring Writer of the Year, pens a weekly column for the Sunday Mirror and writes for many newspapers and magazines.

He's the creator of the Britain's Worst Driver TV format that has been franchised to 14 different countries including America and Canada.

Known as one of the saner motoring commentators with genuine environmental sensibilities he's helped the government launch their electric car trial project and regularly consults with ministers and government agencies on transport policies.

ABOUT THIS BOOK

This book is for anyone who is interested in owning an electric car and who wants to know more about them. If you want to know what an electric car is like to own, use and live with on a day to day basis, you've come to the right place.

The book has taken over three years to research and has been written with input from hundreds of people from all around the world.

From Bangalore to Paris, from Los Angeles to London, electric car owners have contributed their opinions and their experiences to help you make an informed choice about electric cars and whether they could be right for you.

As well as existing electric car owners, I've talked to vehicle manufacturers, car designers and electric vehicle infrastructure specialists from around the world to discover the technology that makes up an electric car.

I've spoken to members of the general public to understand their perceptions of electric cars. They have told me what they believe the positives and negatives of electric cars are and what questions they would want answering before they would consider buying an electric car.

I have worked hard to present a balanced picture of the environmental impact of electric cars. To do this I have worked my way through hundreds of research documents. I've met with electricity producers, key people in the nuclear industry, environmental pressure groups, car manufacturers and petro-chemical companies to ascertain the benefits and detriments of different technologies.

I've also carried out some real world tests myself, comparing two electric cars with two comparable combustion engine cars to see how they measure up in terms of environmental performance.

While the environmental debate is an important one, it is not the sole reason for choosing an electric car. For many current electric car owners environmental considerations were not a significant reason for buying their car.

This book is full of factual, relevant information without the 'techno-babble' that all too often takes over the debate about electric cars. Where I feel it is relevant, I do talk about the different technologies that make up an electric car but only in order to help you make an informed decision about owning and using an electric car.

Scattered through the book you will find a number of very short articles about different businesses and groups that are working in or around the electric vehicle industry. Some of these are examples of companies building electric cars today, or extending the boundaries of the technology; others are working behind the scenes on infrastructure, or enabling the wide scale uptake of electric cars in other ways. These articles are designed to give you an insight into the creation of an exciting new industry and show how electric cars can work in the real world.

The result is this book you now hold in your hands. By the time you have finished reading it you'll understand what it is like to own, use and live with an electric car on a daily basis. You'll understand the benefits and the drawbacks for electric cars and you will know whether or not an electric car is suitable for you.

You'll also know how to avoid the problems that some owners have experienced with their electric cars and ensure you get the best out of owning and using an electric car yourself.

Incidentally, just to avoid any confusion, although the book discusses hybrid and fuel cell cars, the book is specifically about 'pure' electric cars – i.e. cars powered purely by an electric motor and charged by plugging them into a power socket.

About the author

Michael Boxwell is a car enthusiast. He has owned a number of rare and unusual vehicles over the years. These cars include a Pilgrim Bulldog, a 1963 Sunbeam Alpine Mk 3 GT, an ex-RAF 1940 Hartey Dingwell and most recently, a 1954 MG Magnette ZA.

He misspent his youth tinkering with cars and engines in his father's garage and driving racing cars around motor racing circuits.

He has been an advocate for electric vehicles for many years. In the early 2000s he founded an electric bike retail business. This grew to become the largest independent electric bike retailer in the United Kingdom.

He purchased his first electric car in 2006 and founded the REVA/G-Wiz Electric Car Owners' Club the same year. The club is among the largest and most popular electric car owners' clubs in the world with over 1,000 members.

He has provided consultancy for a number of electric vehicle manufacturers and distributors and has travelled around the world visiting electric vehicle production lines and R&D departments.

He regularly speaks and writes about various aspects of electric vehicles and electric vehicle ownership and is a regular guest contributor on the EVcast electric vehicle internet podcast show (www.EVcast.com).

Michael has previously written about solar energy, electric bikes and mobile computing systems.

Michael lives in Warwickshire in the United Kingdom and is married with two children.

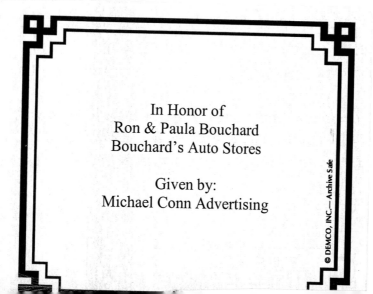

In Honor of
Ron & Paula Bouchard
Bouchard's Auto Stores

Given by:
Michael Conn Advertising

© DEMCO, INC.— Archive Safe

The Making of an Electric Supercar

Creating a new, successful supercar company from scratch is hard work. Some would say it is impossible: the three most recent examples of successful supercar manufacturers are Ferrari in the late 1940s, Porsche in the 1950s and Lamborghini in the 1960s.

Not once since those big three has a new supercar brand managed to appear on the world stage and become a success.

Many have tried. All have failed. Who can remember De Tomatso, Qvale, Lister, Pegaso, Cisitalia, Ascari, Iso, Nazca, Spectre or Gumpert to name but a few?

Yet, one company in California has managed to buck the trend, creating an exciting brand and new sports car from scratch.

The company is Tesla, and the car is their remarkable Tesla Roadster.

The car combines stunning good looks with mind blowing performance. The statistics speak for themselves: the standard Tesla Roadster can out accelerate a Lamborghini Murcielago LP460 or a Ferrari 612 Scaglietti. It will leave almost anything built by Porsche standing. The new Tesla Sport model is even faster still.

Tesla has had to overcome incredible odds. Yet in less than two years since the first car was delivered to its first customer, Tesla has become a huge success story. With a starting price of $109,000 in the US, and €99,000 in Europe the car has been selling strongly with production booked out for months in advance. The Tesla brand has become one of the hottest brands in America and the car has become the darling of the Hollywood set.

So what has made Tesla buck the trend? Quite simply, their car is unique. In a world where fast cars mean petrol power, Tesla has built an electric car.

The car is a revelation to everyone who drives it. From the massive punch of adrenaline-inducing power to the 'jet fighter' scream of its electric motor, the Tesla Roadster redefines the electric car.

Tesla has shown that electric cars can be fast, powerful and exciting. With a range of 240 miles and a fast charging capability, the car also has an answer for all the objections that most people have for an electric car.

Today, Tesla sells cars in the United States, Canada and Europe with exclusive showrooms in cities like San Diego, Los Angeles, Chicago, Seattle, Monaco and London.

Next year, Tesla launches a luxury four door saloon with sports car performance and looks. They will be taking on the best that BMW, Mercedes, Maserati and Jaguar can produce.

Will they succeed? Very few people would bet against them...

INTRODUCING THE ELECTRIC CAR

It seems every week electric cars are hitting the headlines. From car makers showing their latest concepts, governments announcing new incentive schemes and announcements of new technology breakthroughs, electric cars appear to be everywhere. Yet when was the last time you saw an electric car on the road?

The chances are you may never have seen one at all. Unless you live in the centre of London, Paris or Bangalore, the three 'electric car capitals' of the world, electric cars in actual daily use are few and far between.

Electric cars are nothing new. The first electric cars were built almost 175 years ago. At the beginning of the 20th Century, electric cars were the best selling cars around.

In more recent history, major manufacturers like Ford, Toyota, Fiat, Citroen, Peugeot and General Motors have all built electric cars. In the 1990s, each of these manufacturers built small numbers of electric cars and offered them on sale or to rent to the general public. Many of these cars are still on the roads today and often find their way onto the used car market.

Electric cars have remained a niche product. If the publicity and the policymakers are to be believed, all that will change over the next two or three years. Almost every car maker now has active electric car development projects, with the majority of these cars scheduled to appear between now and 2015.

New electric cars are already available from a number of specialist car makers and they are making inroads into the market. Manufacturers like GEM, Tesla, Aixam and REVA have been building cars for years, and Mitsubishi has recently launched their first electric car.

What is an electric car?

An electric car is a car powered by an electric motor, typically powered using energy stored in a battery. An electric car does not have a combustion engine. It is charged by plugging it into an electricity socket.

Most electric cars do not have a conventional gearbox. Instead, the electric motor powers the wheels, either directly or through a simple differential. As a consequence, electric cars have very few moving parts. Some electric car manufacturers claim their cars have as few as 15-20 moving parts compared to several hundred in a car powered by a combustion engine.

Electrical energy is typically stored in a bank of batteries built into the car. The batteries are relatively bulky and heavy, taking up about the same amount of space and weighing a little more than an engine and gearbox in a conventional car.

Charging time depends on the type of power socket you have. Charging a car from a domestic socket typically takes between 5–10 hours. 'Fast charging' through a dedicated high voltage, high current electricity supply can often charge an electric car in less than an hour.

How an electric car compares to a conventional car

While electric cars are not for everyone or every application, for many people, electric cars are the ideal vehicle and offer significant benefits over other types of cars.

At the heart of an electric car is the electric motor. In terms of construction and power delivery it is almost the complete opposite to a combustion engine:

	Electric Motor	Combustion Engine
Average Efficiency	90% plus	25-35%
Maximum Power	From Standstill	At high speed
Multi-ratio gearbox required	Rarely	Always
Number of moving parts	2-3	130+

8

By taking these characteristics into account, we can understand why driving a car with an electric motor is different to driving a car with an internal combustion engine. In the main, this means that electric cars are a more pleasant driving experience than their combustion engine counterparts:

- Maximum power from a standing start means an electric car pulls away smoothly and quickly. You don't have to rev the engine to pull away.

- The lack of a gearbox makes for easy driving with a smooth power delivery.

- Electric motors are exceptionally quiet and have no vibration.

- In most electric cars, the motor is used to slow the car down when you brake:

  o The forward momentum of the car is used to recharge the batteries and slow the car down at the same time.

  o The conventional mechanical braking system is often only needed under heavy braking.

  o The result is much smoother and more progressive braking and a smoother transition between accelerating and braking.

- In heavy stop-start traffic, electric cars are just easier to drive. They can crawl along at low speeds very efficiently with minimal effort on the part of the driver.

- At lower speeds, electric cars feel more responsive with instant throttle response and predictable power delivery.

Some electric cars have a reduced top speed when compared to combustion engine cars. A number of electric cars are designed purely for inner city use and have performance to match. This is ideal to travel with the ebb and flow of traffic in a busy city but not enough for longer journeys.

When driving fast on high speed roads and freeways, electric cars are at another disadvantage. The amount of energy required to travel at high speed means the range per charge can drop significantly compared to lower speed use.

Electric cars are in their element in built up areas such as cities, urban and sub-urban environments where speeds are limited and there is a lot of stop-start driving.

That does not mean they cannot be used anywhere else. There are many electric cars are entirely suitable for both short and medium distance higher speed driving:

- The Tesla Roadster has a range of around 240 miles (380km) and a top speed of 135mph (216km/h). 0-60mph (0-100km/h) takes under 4 seconds

- The Mitsubishi i-MiEV and Nissan Leaf are all comfortably capable of cruising at 75-80mph (120-130km/h).

Is range the weakest point of an electric car?

You can't discuss electric cars for very long before the discussion focuses on the range of an electric car. Wherever you go around the world, it is the number one concern that non-electric car owners have about owning an electric car.

The reality is quite often very different from the perception. Many electric car owners will actually describe the freedom they feel that every time they go out to their cars in the morning. They know they have enough 'fuel' to go wherever they want to without the hassle and cost of visiting the filling station to refuel.

One electric car owner explains it like this: "It takes me nine seconds to charge up my electric car. That's the time it takes to plug the car in when I get home. The next time I need to use the car, it is charged up."

The majority of electric cars that are available today have a range of between 40 miles (65km) and 100 miles (160km), which is far more than most people travel on a regular basis:

- According to the UK Department for Transport, that the average car journey is 6½ miles (10½km) with 93% of all car journeys being less than 25 miles (40km).

- According to the US Department of Transportation, an average American driver travels 29 miles (46½km) per day by car, with an average single journey of around 12 miles (19km).

- Many people never travel more than 50 miles (80km) from their homes and many more will only travel further than 50 miles a few times each year.

For most electric cars, the 'charging point' required is usually a standard domestic power socket. Many electric car owners have been able to arrange to plug in to charge up their cars when they are at their destination (such as at work), thereby removing any range concerns and enabling them to travel further.

A full charge from a domestic socket typically takes between 5 and 10 hours, depending on both the car and the country (North America has 110v mains supply whereas the rest of the world has a 220v supply which can charge up electric cars faster). Many electric cars can provide an 80% charge in around 2–2½ hours from a domestic socket.

Some electric cars can also be fast charged using a dedicated charging point. These charging points provide a much higher current in order to charge up batteries faster. A fast charge typically allows your car to be charged to 80% of its capacity within 30-45 minutes.

It is interesting to compare the concerns that non-electric car owners have about range with the perceptions that existing electric car owners have about range:

- Non-electric car owners perceive that range is going to be a constant issue. They believe that they will be restricted because they cannot simply visit a filling station to refuel their cars.

- Electric car owners like the fact that every time they go out to use their car it is fully charged up and ready to go. They have enough fuel to go wherever they need to and they'll never have to visit a filling station ever again.

If you are regularly travelling a longer distance between two points, between home and work for example, having a charging point at your destination may solve the problem. For instance, if you have an electric car with a range of 80 miles (130km), you can double this range if you can charge the car up again at your destination.

11

Several electric car owners use their cars for lots of short journeys throughout the day. The combined distance travelled during the day can be far greater than the range of the car if the car can be plugged in and recharged whenever it is parked.

Of course, there are always people who have to regularly travel longer distances to different locations in their cars and for these people a better solution may be a hybrid car, or a range extended electric car once these become available.

If you only need a long distance car occasionally, once a month or so, there are solutions available to you. Car manufacturers and governments are both working hard to provide solutions for people who may need to travel longer distances on an occasional basis:

- Many countries already have a network of charging points in place. Some of these have been provided by government, some have been provided by industry and some have been provided by groups of electric car enthusiasts:
  - Many cities already have charging points, either at road sides or in car parks. Some cities, such as London and Paris, have plans to install tens of thousands of additional charging points over the next few years.
  - Various companies are building a network of fast charging points that can charge up electric cars in around 30-45 minutes.
  - Some shopping malls are introducing charging points and priority parking for electric car owners.
  - In the UK, there is a network of charging points that has been set up and run by enthusiasts. This has become one of the most comprehensive charging networks anywhere in the world!

- Electric car owners and clubs have worked with local businesses such as bars, restaurants and shopping malls to promote electric car charging points.

- Many electric car owners have also come to an arrangement with their employer to provide them with charging facilities at work.

- A company called Better Place, backed by Renault and Nissan, are building an infrastructure of battery swap-out stations. With this technology, flat batteries from Better Place equipped cars can be swapped out for fully charged batteries in around 3 minutes.

- REVA, an electric car manufacturer, has built a charging interface into their vehicle that allows owners to connect to their car via their mobile phone:
    - If the car is parked and on charge, the car can notify the owner when the car is fully charged and ready to go.
    - If the car is running flat, the owner can send a text to the manufacturer who will then check the batteries remotely and unlock a virtual reserve tank to add additional range to the car.

- Some electric car manufacturers now sell their electric cars with a 'car club' plan. These car clubs allow the electric car owner to get access to another car if they need to travel for longer distances and an electric car is not suitable.

- Car Clubs are becoming popular in many cities. These clubs allow you to have access to a car hourly or daily on a 'pay as you use' basis. These clubs are ideal for people who only occasionally need a long distance vehicle and the cars can normally be booked with very little notice.

Are electric cars the silent killer?

Every electric car owner I have met has said that they are always very aware of the lack of engine noise when driving. It is seen as one of the major benefits of electric cars. The lack of noise significantly reduces stress levels in a lot of people, making the whole driving experience a lot more enjoyable.

When questioned, electric car owners say they are very aware that at low speeds, their cars are very quiet. They say that they make sure they give other road users more space and take more care when driving in areas where there are a lot of cyclists and pedestrians.

If you are outside the car, however, it isn't actually as quiet as you may expect. Some electric cars have a fan that run whenever the motor is powering the car which can clearly be heard by pedestrians. At speeds above 10mph the car can be heard through road noise and wind noise.

In built up areas where an electric car is travelling so slowly that it cannot be heard, it is usually not the only silent vehicle on the roads. Bicycles are virtually silent as well, yet they are involved with fewer accidents with pedestrians than any other form of transport.

Furthermore, when driving at walking pace, most combustion engine cars are virtually silent and cannot be heard by pedestrians.

Road noise and wind noise are actually louder than you may expect. In the vast majority of modern cars, the in car insulation stops you from being aware of these noises from inside the car. When you are standing by the side of a road, however, it is the road and wind noise of the cars passing you that you hear, rather than the engine noise.

Don't believe me? Go and stand by the side of a road with high speed traffic. What traffic sounds do you hear?

- If you're hearing a 'whoosh' sound, that is the sound of the air splitting and then reforming around the car as it travels.

- If you hear a lower pitched rumble, similar to the friction sound when you drag your feet slowly along the ground, you are hearing the sound of the rubber on the road surface.

- Unless a car is in a low gear and accelerating heavily, the chances are you won't hear the engine until the car is next to you.

The claim that electric cars are 'silent killers' appears to be a myth and concerns about this being a future problem appears to be based more a perceived issue rather than a real problem. I have not been able to find any record of any deaths or serious injuries anywhere in the world that have been attributed to the silence of an electric car.

I recently asked a member for the UK Parliamentary Advisory Council for Transport Safety (PACTS) for his own personal opinion about the issue of silent electric cars and his personal belief was that this is not an issue.

I also spoke with a car designer who used to work with blind people and his personal view is that silent electric cars pose no greater risk to blind people than other road transport.

I have been using electric vehicles for seven years. Four years with an electric car and three years with electric bikes. I have not once experienced a problem caused by pedestrians not hearing me.

Other forms of electric cars

If you are a driver who regularly needs to travel long distance and an electric car is out of the question because of range, there are two other options available to you: hydrogen 'fuel cell' cars and hybrid cars.

Hydrogen 'fuel cell' cars

Figure 1 - The Honda FCX Clarity - the first hydrogen fuel cell car available to the general public from a major manufacturer.

Hydrogen fuel cell cars are electric cars where hydrogen powered fuel cells generates electricity to top up the batteries.

As a consequence, the driving characteristics of fuel cell vehicles are the same as electric vehicles.

A fuel cell is a power generator that produces electricity through chemical reaction with fuel (hydrogen in the case of vehicles) as opposed to burning the fuel, as with a combustion engine.

Fuel cells typically extract twice as much power from their fuel source than combustion engines but run at a much slower rate.

At present, very few hydrogen fuel cell cars exist. Honda is currently leasing small numbers of their FCX Clarity fuel cell car in California, Japan and Germany, and a handful of Microcab fuel cell city cars are being tested in the United Kingdom.

During the first half of 2010, Honda will start supplying the FCX Clarity in other parts of the US and the UK.

The perceived benefit of fuel cell cars are that they can be refilled quickly at any available hydrogen fuelling station. In reality hydrogen fuel stations simply do not exist. Worldwide, there are currently only 80 hydrogen filling stations open to the public. The majority of these are in Iceland, with a handful more in California and the United Kingdom.

Hydrogen fuel stations are likely to become more common over the next few years. However, it is going to take a very significant amount of time before they are a common sight on our roads. There are also question marks about the environmental benefits of hydrogen powered cars:

- Hydrogen fuel cell cars are emission free at the point of use but the extraction of hydrogen in the first place is a very energy intensive process.

- For instance, extracting hydrogen from water through electrolysis requires three units of electricity for every unit of hydrogen you generate.

- This is not a problem in countries where electricity is abundant and carbon friendly. Iceland, for example, is already installing a hydrogen infrastructure for the next generation of fuel cell cars.

In the short term, Honda is planning to provide early FCX Clarity users with their own hydrogen charging stations in their own homes. Creating hydrogen from natural gas, owners will have a range of around 250 miles (400km) from a tank of hydrogen.

However, these hydrogen stations will not be environmentally friendly. Experts estimate that hydrogen created this way for use in the FCX Clarity will be around 50% less environmentally friendly than using an equivalent conventional combustion engine car.

Using hydrogen in a combustion engine

Several manufacturers, including Ford and BMW, have developed cars that can use liquid hydrogen in a modified combustion engine car. These promise zero emissions from the vehicle, using a combustion engine rather than fuel cells:

- The build price for this type of hydrogen car is lower than a fuel cell car as it is built using existing mass-produced technology.

- Hydrogen powered combustion engines are half as efficient as hydrogen fuel cells, meaning and more fuel stops.

- Until hydrogen fuel stations become widespread, hydrogen combustion engine cars are likely to remain concept cars only.

Hybrid cars

Hybrid cars combine an electric motor with a combustion engine, using the electric motor to assist the combustion engine during acceleration and for low speed driving.

There are two alternative types of hybrid cars. Hybrid cars like the Toyota Prius and Honda Insight are known as 'parallel' hybrids. The electric motor and the engine work in parallel to power the car. In other words, either electric motor or engine can turn the wheels.

A 'series' hybrid car is different. A series hybrid is an electric car where only the electric motor powers the wheels. The combustion engine then powers a generator to top-up the batteries when required. Series hybrids are the basis for 'range extended electric cars' which will start arriving in showrooms soon.

Range Extended electric cars

Later this year, Chevrolet launches the Volt in North America. Opel and Vauxhall will launch the European version in 2011.

The Volt is an electric car with an electric-only range of up to 40 miles. Once the batteries are flat, combustion engine kicks in and recharges the batteries when the car is still on the move.

Although the efficiency of these vehicles are not match for full electric vehicles, cars like the Volt has the potential to offer a good solution for people wanting an electric car but where the ability to travel longer distances on a regular basis is also important.

Do hybrid cars provide the best of both worlds?

Hybrid car enthusiasts claim that hybrids provide the best of both worlds, combining a practical long distance car that can cruise at freeway speeds all day long with an electric car for town use.

The current generation of hybrid cars, however, only has a very short electric-only range – typically 1-2 miles. Future hybrid cars, such as the Chevrolet Volt, promise much longer ranges.

Many hybrids (referred to as mild hybrids) use the combustion engine all the time, using the electric motor to supplement the engine. These cars cannot be used in 'electric car only' mode.

With all current hybrid models, the batteries are charged up using the both combustion engine and regenerative braking. Although using an engine to charge batteries is more efficient than using an engine to drive the wheels, it still means the electric element of the vehicle is powered using fossil fuels.

The production cost and energy required in producing hybrid cars is higher than other cars as they have both a combustion engine and an electric motor and batteries in the same vehicle. However, this is still a relatively insignificant impact to the environment when compared to running a car (see page 139 for more information on the environmental impact of car production).

The motor industry generally regards hybrid vehicles as a short to medium term measure before long range electric cars and fuel-cell cars are the norm.

For regular long distance driving, where pure electric cars are currently not suitable, hybrid cars do have several benefits over non-hybrid combustion engine cars.

How hybrid cars compare with economical diesel cars

Across Europe, diesel powered cars have become popular for long distance driving. A modern diesel car is very economical and has comparatively low carbon dioxide emissions. From a driving perspective, they can be ideal long distance vehicles.

From an economy perspective, diesel powered cars can provide similar long distance economy to current hybrid cars. For this reason, a lot of people believe that hybrid cars are irrelevant.

This only shows part of the benefit of a hybrid car, however:

- For long distance driving, hybrid cars and diesel cars provide similar economy.

- Around town, a hybrid car provides significantly improved economy, as the electric motor takes away much of the stresses from the combustion engine.

The biggest benefit of hybrid cars over diesel cars comes from the improved overall emissions from the car, of which carbon dioxide is just one.

We'll cover the issue of diesel pollution in more detail later on in the book when we look at Electric Cars and the Environment (see page 107 for more information on Diesel Pollution).

Chapter Summary

- Electric cars are increasingly regarded as being the 'next big thing' by the car industry and governments alike.

- Electric cars are already available today.

- Electric cars have different driving characteristics to cars fitted with a combustion engine.

- Electric cars are in their element in cities and urban areas, although that doesn't stop them being driven elsewhere.

- Concerns about range are seen as a problem by non owners but rarely an issue with owners.

- There are various options available for travelling longer distances when you drive an electric car.

- Hydrogen 'fuel cell' cars are electric cars with a fuel cell generating power that tops up the batteries, which in turn powers the car.

- Hybrid cars reduce the environmental impact of the combustion engine but do not eradicate it.

- Hybrids are significantly better than diesel powered cars in terms of environmental efficiency and currently offer the best solution for frequent long distance drivers from an environmental viewpoint.

Mitsubishi have won the race to be the first mainstream car manufacturer to launch a next-generation electric car. The i-MiEV (pronounced eye-meev) is a very capable small family car that takes the electric car out of the city. Better still, if you live in Japan or the United Kingdom, you can have one today.

Equally at home on the freeway or the city, the i--MiEV (Mitsubishi Innovative Electric Vehicle) is a fast, quiet and practical family runabout.

Put on sale in Japan and the United Kingdom in late 2009, the i-MiEV has created a huge amount of renewed interest in electric cars. Celebrities Quentin Willson and Robert Llewellyn both use i-MiEVs and UK applications from customers to buy the first batch of cars were ten times oversubscribed.

The i-MiEV is a spacious sub-compact, four seat city car with enough interior space for the average family and their luggage.

The power comes from a 47kW electric motor, powered by 16kWh of lithium batteries.

Performance is brisk. 0-62mph (0-100km/h) takes around 13 seconds – 5 seconds faster than the conventional combustion engine version of the car. Top speed is 82mph (132km/h) and the car has a range of 100 miles (160km).

To drive, the car is exactly like a combustion engine car with automatic gearbox. Drivers of conventional automatic cars will feel right at home.

"One of the things that we decided very early on was that the car needs to be near to a current normal car as possible," says Lance Bradley, Managing Director of Mitsubishi Motors UK. "We've made it like an ordinary car, the only difference is that there aren't any emissions out of it and it doesn't make any noise."

In taking that approach, some electric car purists argue that Mitsubishi have compromised some of the benefits and ease of use of an electric car. Yet, the car remains an exceptionally good vehicle that manages to be better than its combustion engine equivalent.

There is no doubt that the i-MiEV is a very important new car. It is the first of a new generation of electric cars that will bring electric cars into the mainstream.

LIVING WITH AN ELECTRIC CAR

First impressions

The first time you step inside an electric car and drive away, it feels very strange!

Most electric cars don't have a gearbox, so the gear lever usually resembles an automatic. In some cases, the gear lever has been replaced by a switch allowing you to select forward or reverse.

Once you switch on the ignition, there is no noise or faint vibration to let you know the engine is running. Most people are unsure whether the car is actually ready to pull away or not. As you tentatively put the car into *Drive* and touch the accelerator, there is a mild sense of shock that the car pulls away virtually silently.

It takes a few minutes to get used to the strange sensation of travelling without an engine noise. At speeds below 10mph, the car makes very little noise and as a driver you are aware of that. In fact, you will probably be more aware of that than anyone around you as most modern cars are very quiet at walking speeds anyhow.

As the speeds increase, road noise and wind noise now mean that your electric car is making virtually the same amount of noise to the outside world as any other car. Inside the car, the impression is still that the car is exceptionally quiet because you cannot hear an engine and most modern cars have high quality insulation to keep road noise and wind noise out of the cabin as much as possible.

Performance

Once you are used to the silence, you start noticing other things. The power delivery is very smooth and there is no vibration from the engine.

As you drive the car, you will start noticing how good low-speed performance is. Electric cars are usually very quick when pulling away and driving around town can be an enjoyable experience. The vast majority of electric cars provide excellent around town performance.

At higher speeds, on open roads and freeways, electric cars may feel under powered. This is not the case with all electric cars but in many cases high speed performance is usually adequate rather than brisk.

The Fun factor

Most people who have never driven an electric car are quite surprised by how much fun an electric car can be.

Your average electric car won't win a race away from the traffic lights against a Porsche (although an electric sports car like the Tesla Roadster certainly would!). Yet in their natural environment of a town or a city, they are surprisingly nippy. As the heavy batteries are mounted low down in the chassis, they also have a low centre of gravity, often making for reasonable handling.

For example, the Mitsubishi i-MiEV electric car is immensely fun to drive around town. The spritely performance, responsive steering and sharp handling make for an entertaining and enjoyable driving experience.

Braking

Braking for the first time can be strange experience in an electric car. Most electric cars have two braking systems, combining 'regenerative braking' with a standard braking system. As described in the previous chapter, regenerative braking uses the momentum of the car to generate power which is put back into the batteries.

Different manufacturers implement regenerative braking in different ways. The best systems build regenerative braking into the brake pedal of the car. To slow down, you put your foot on the brake pedal and all the power is then fed back into the batteries to extend your range. The mechanical brakes are only used if you have to stop quickly.

In other electric cars, you have to move the gear lever to a different position in order to deploy regenerative braking. In these systems, you have to make a conscious decision to slow the car down using regenerative braking. These systems are not so intuitive to use and do take a lot more time to get used to.

Range Fixation

It isn't long on your first drive before you become aware of the fuel gauge. In fact, if you've never driven an electric car before, the fuel gauge almost always becomes a fixation for the first few weeks.

An electric car has a shorter range than a combustion engine car, so the fuel gauge moves quicker than you will first expect.

In most combustion engine cars the fuel gauge seems to stay close to full for the first half tank of fuel and then move down quite rapidly afterwards. In any car, once the fuel gauge drops below a quarter, many people start getting 'range fixation'. They're on the lookout for a fuel station and starting to worry if they can't find one on their route.

In an electric car, the fuel gauge will start to move after only a few miles of driving. It is a bit disconcerting at first because everyone is so used to the way fuel gauges work in conventional cars. In effect, you are getting the same range fixation as you do when running low on fuel in any other car.

Even when you're driving a short distance and you absolutely *know* there is enough charge to get to your destination, it is very easy to get fixated on the fuel gauge in the early days.

It's a psychological difference. In reality, you are no more likely to run out of range in an electric car than you are to run out of fuel in a normal car. The best analogy to use is that of a mobile phone. If you plug your phone in overnight to charge it up, it doesn't let you down. The same is true with an electric car.

Once you've got more confidence in your electric car and you have used it for a while, your range fixation disappears.

In fact, you get to the point where you ignore the fuel gauge completely. After all, if you plug your car in every night and you know that you've got enough range to do your daily driving, why bother checking the fuel gauge?

Range Fixation with a brand new electric car

The issue of range fixation is worse on a brand new electric car than with a used car.

If you have a brand new electric car, the batteries will need to be used a few times to build up the range. You won't get your maximum range until the batteries have gone through a few charge-discharge cycles. When the car leaves the showroom, your car may only do around half to two-thirds of its advertised range.

If you are not aware of this problem, this compounds the problem of range fixation. It certainly doesn't do much for confidence in your new car!

The range will improve within a few days and continue to improve over the following weeks. Within a few weeks, your batteries will be improved and your range will be significantly better.

Plugging It In

Most electric cars have a socket on the outside of the car. Sometimes this is hidden behind a flap in the radiator grill; sometimes it is behind a fuel filler cap.

The power cable for the vast

A Clever Idea

As a leading electric car maker, REVA has more experience than most when it comes to understanding car owners' fears about range.

"We know from our customers around the world that one of the key barriers is this 'range anxiety' – fear that you're going to run out of charge in an electric car", says Keith Johnston, President of European Operations for the REVA Electric Car Company. "We know in reality you are no more likely to do that in an electric car than you are in a conventional car."

To counter this fear, REVA have used technology to provide the answer: instead of having a conventional fuel gauge, the latest REVA NXR shows you how much distance you have remaining, in either miles or km.

REVA have also developed a unique technology called Revive Emergency Charge. Revive uses the remote diagnostics technology built into the car to monitor the batteries and provide additional power if required. If an owner is driving the car and they see themselves running very low on range, they can simply text REVA from their mobile phone.

REVA then remotely check the state of the batteries and releases additional energy from the batteries. The customer will then see the range going up by a few miles so they can continue on their journey.

majority of electric cars plugs straight into a standard household power socket. You can buy an external socket for the outside wall of your home if you do not have a garage.

A few electric cars have a dedicated high-current power outlet in order to charge the cars quickly. These may consist simply of a high current industrial socket fitted to a wall, or may be a complete external car charger.

Electric cars that have a high-current power charger also have the ability to charge from a standard household socket. This means that you can charge away from home should you need to.

It feels very strange to plug your car in for the very first time. It is a novelty that takes some time to wear off.

The first few weeks

The first few weeks with an electric car are fun. The novelty factor of a car that runs on electricity lasts a while and in general, most electric cars are a lot of fun to drive.

You go through a period where you are thinking about every journey you are going on. You are constantly checking that you have enough range and often making arrangements to plug your car into a power socket at your destination, even if your destination is well within the range of the car.

It is all part of the 'range fixation' that you get as a new electric car driver. It soon wears off.

One thing that happens to most people at some point in the first few weeks is forgetting to plug the car in. Most people do it once and usually at the most inconvenient time. Thankfully, if your journey is relatively short, you can often plug your car in and get enough range after 20-30 minutes of charging to get you to your destination. As a consequence, the results are rarely catastrophic but most electric car owners rarely make the same mistake twice!

If most of your driving is around a town or city, you will find the performance of your electric car is great. Acceleration from a standing start is usually quick and the cars can be fun to drive in and around town.

If you have bought a *neighborhood electric vehicle*[1] (NEV) in the United States, then your car can only be used in and around towns and cities. Your top speed on an NEV is limited but even so, you will find that most of the time you are keeping up with the rest of the traffic flow around you.

If you have bought a used electric car, you may find that some older models of electric car are sluggish when going up hills and that their performance is limiting when driving out of town. Most new electric cars have resolved those problems and will drive along at a reasonable speed both in town and out on faster roads.

Speed and Range

As with any other car, economy figures depend on how you drive the car. If you drive everywhere as fast as possible, you will not get the same range as you will if you drive economically.

However, there are other factors that do make a difference to the range of an electric car. Running heating or air conditioning will make a difference (although some electric cars have a diesel powered heater) but less obviously ambient temperature can also make a difference. Batteries perform better in warm weather than they do in very cold conditions.

Using lights or radio in the car will make very little difference to range. These ancillaries use relatively insignificant amounts of electricity compared to the amount of energy used by the electric motor.

Most electric car manufacturers are wary of claiming unfeasibly long ranges for their cars, as to do so would damage customer confidence in their products but it is also true that to achieve the maximum range, some drivers have to adjust their driving styles and techniques in order to achieve them. These adjustments are not difficult and many people adopt them without even being aware that they have done so.

During the first few weeks, most drivers experiment with different driving styles to see how much they can improve the range

---

[1] See our chapter on *Electric Cars you can Drive Today* on page 48 for more information on the different categories of electric cars

of their cars. Even if they don't need the maximum range from the car, many drivers feel a sense of achievement by getting the absolute maximum range out of their electric car.

As with fuel economy on any type of car, the biggest single difference you can make to range is adjust your speed. The faster you go, the greater the wind resistance and the shorter distance you'll be able to drive. Conversely, the slower you travel, the further you'll be able to go.

The calculation is not linear but as a general rule if you reduce your speed by 10% you'll be able to increase your range by around 15%.

Another good example of how a driver may adjust their driving techniques with an electric car is with braking:

- In combustion engine cars, a huge amount of kinetic energy is lost when you apply the brake pedal. The energy is converted to heat through brake friction.

- In an electric car, regenerative braking uses the speed of the vehicle to power the motor, which in turn generates electricity that charges the batteries, running the entire system in reverse to generate electricity.

- In many electric cars, regenerative braking can handle most of the braking effort required in day-to-day driving. I recently heard of one electric car owner whose 25 year old electric car is still on its original brake pads!

- In a city environment, using regenerative braking effectively can increase the range of most electric cars by up to 30%.

Naturally, it takes time for a new electric car driver to get used to regenerative braking and to learn how to use it as effectively as possible.

Freedom from the service station

After driving an electric car for a few weeks, you see that every time you get up in the morning you have a car with a 'tank full' of electricity and the freedom to drive wherever you want to drive during that day.

Suddenly, the benefits of being able to recharge your car at home rather than having to drive to a service station to refuel become apparent. No longer are you worrying about range; rather you are seeing the benefits of always having a car with a tank full of electricity every morning and never having to pay for fuel at a service station.

Borrowing a 'plug full' of electricity

At some point during your electric car ownership, you will ask a friend if you can charge up your car when you're visiting. Most people are more than happy to 'lend a plug'. When people know that you are driving an electric car, many people will offer without being asked. Friends are often quite surprised if you don't need the charge and turn them down!

The cost for the electricity your borrowing is likely to be in the region of 10-20 cents per hour in the US, or 15-25p per hour in the UK during peak times.

If you use your electric car for business, you will often find that businesses are also more than happy to offer a charge up when you are visiting them. It is always best to phone up and ask first, to make sure that it is convenient.

If you are visiting a remote pub, restaurant or even an independent hotel in the evening, you will find that most of them are more than happy to offer a charge up in return for your custom. I always recommend you phone up and ask first, don't just turn up and expect them to accommodate you.

Camping and caravanning sites have onsite electricity, although if you are in Europe, you will require a 16 amp industrial plug in order to connect to it. Many sites have been happy to offer electric car charging for a small fee when requested.

If you want to borrow electricity in this way, make sure you have a suitable extension lead with you that can take the current required for charging up an electric car. The lead should not be coiled during charging as this can create a dangerous heat build up in the car. Make sure that the lead also has a RCD protected plug and that the socket to plug your standard car charging cable in is protected from the elements.

Charging at work

Many electric car owners make arrangements with their employers to allow them to charge up their cars from work. Many employers are happy to provide this freely as it portrays the company as being environmentally friendly. In other cases, the electric car owner has to pay their employer for the electricity used.

There are cases where charging your car at work causes petty jealousies with other members of staff, who see it as getting something for free that they can't have themselves.

Offering to contribute to the company for the electricity, or offering to pay a small donation to charity instead almost always resolves this problem.

Quite often, an external power socket will need to be installed in order to allow an electric car to be charged up regularly. The cost of this will vary from site to site but is rarely expensive.

Electric Car charging points

In many countries, more and more towns and cities are now installing electric car charging points. Charging points are being built into retail shopping areas, car parks and at roadside parking facilities.

Around the world, local government and town councils are under pressure to make electric car charging points available. The pressure is coming from politicians, environmental groups, and car manufacturers and from many electricity companies. Charging post solutions are available from several post manufacturers and many new inner city developments currently at the design stage are being designed to ensure they are electric vehicle friendly.

Businesses too are offering charging facilities for customers too. Restaurants, pubs, hotels, shops and service stations are starting to offer charging facilities, often free of charge for customers and for a small fee for other owners.

The United Kingdom is leading the way, with charging facilities in dozens of towns and cities around the country, with thousands of new charging locations planned for the near future. Combined with the EV Network initiative, the United Kingdom is close to having its own nationwide charging network already in place.

At present, all of the public charging points in place around the United Kingdom are available free of charge to electric car owners. Most public charging points and charging points run by shopping malls and retail parks allow you to simply turn up and plug in.

However, most council run charging points in London require you to register for access to the charging points before you can use them. In return for registering, you receive an electronic key to unlock the charging point and a special car charging cable.

Long Distance Driving

Driving for very long distances on a regular basis is obviously not a practical option for electric cars at the present.

Of course, if your destination is within range of your car and you are going to be parked for several hours before returning, it may be an option to charge up your car at your destination. This can effectively double the range of your electric car. This means that a car with a practical range of 80 miles (130km) can then travel twice that distance in a single day.

A number of electric car owners do lots of short journeys throughout a day. When added together, the overall distance travelled is significantly further than a single charge will allow them to go. In between journeys, the car is placed on charge in order to extend the range, often being charged from customer sites and creating a virtually limitless range.

At time of writing, no country currently has a fast charging network in place to allow electric cars to be charged up within just a few minutes. This will change over the coming years, allowing electric car owners to recharge up to 80% of their battery in 15-20 minutes.

As it is usually a good idea to factor in regular breaks on a long journey, fast charging stations will allow electric cars to become a practical solution for much longer distance journeys.

Meanwhile, a few die-hard enthusiasts have managed to travel much further distances by stopping on their journey for 1-2 hours in order to boost-charge their cars. I know several people who have managed to travel 120-140 miles in a single day with an electric car with a nominal range of just 40 miles!

Long Term Ownership

There have been electric cars on the road now for a number of years. Many electric car owners have now owned electric cars for five years or more and a number are on their second or third electric car.

When asked what they like about their electric cars, many owners talk about the lack of stress when driving an electric car. They are easy to drive, very smooth and quiet. Several owners report that this combines to make driving a much more pleasurable and calming experience.

Many owners also talk about the cost savings of driving an electric car as well as the convenience of being able to charge their cars at home and never having to go to a service station for fuel.

Range is hardly ever mentioned with long term owners. It quite simply isn't regarded as an issue:

- In some cases, the electric car is a second car and therefore the electric car is not used for long distance journeys.

- In other cases, the owners do not travel long distances by car at all, using the train instead.

- Some owners hire a car or belong to a car club for the rare times they need to travel longer distances.

The lack of a nationwide charging infrastructure is also not regarded as an issue. Only a comparatively small number of current electric car owners use the electric car charging points that already exist. Many see very little need in having a charging point network at all.

As batteries get older, the range of the electric car deteriorates. In cold weather the range can also be adversely affected:

- With lead acid and nickel metal hydride batteries, the range will typically drop by 35-40% by the time the batteries need replacing.

- Lithium-ion batteries are much better but will deteriorate by around 20-25% of their original range by the time the batteries need replacing.

- With both lead acid and lithium-ion batteries, you can often continue using the same batteries but the range will continue to decrease until eventually the car grinds to a halt.

- In very cold weather, range can drop by a further 25%.

The main issue that long term ownership has highlighted is the replacement cost of batteries. While the cost of charging batteries and replacing them is still cheaper than fuelling a conventional car, when batteries need replacing, the capital cost can be very considerable:

- Lead acid batteries typically need replacing every three years.

- Nickel Metal Hydride (NiMH) batteries typically need replacing every six to ten years.

- Lithium Ion batteries typically need replacing every six to twelve years, depending on their structure.

The electric vehicle industry has responded to this issue with their latest models. Many new electric cars have battery leasing schemes in place, which aim to resolve this issue. The cost of these battery leases is typically cheaper than buying fuel from a service station for a combustion engine car.

Vehicle manufacturers are also offering longer battery guarantees. In a few cases the batteries are being guaranteed for up to ten years to safeguard electric car owners from unexpected battery maintenance costs.

A second issue that many long term owners have had is with the lack of available electric vehicle servicing agents. Although the mechanical aspects of an electric car are similar to any other car, the electrics and electronics are specific to electric cars and have to be taken to a specialist service agent for maintenance.

This second issue is starting to resolve itself as more car dealers are starting to sell and service electric cars but it is still a valid point when considering whether to buy an electric car or not.

We will look at purchasing and running costs of an electric car in a later chapter (see page 45).

When questioned, the vast majority of people who have owned an electric car for two years or longer are so pleased with them they intend to buy another electric car when they replace their existing model.

Chapter Summary

- Owning and using an electric car is a new experience, which takes a little time to adapt to.

- There is a lot to like about an electric car: the smooth acceleration, the lack of engine noise or vibration, the lack of noise or pollution from the car itself and the fun factor.

- New owners usually suffer from 'range fixation' which is overcome as confidence in the car increases.

- Nearly everybody forgets to plug in the car... once! Very few people forget a second time.

- There are various options available for charging up the car when travelling around. Some people use this to travel surprisingly long distances in a day.

- Very few long term electric car owners regard range as an issue.

- The main two concerns with long term electric car owners has been the replacement costs of batteries and the lack of electric vehicle servicing agents.

  o These two issues are now being addressed by the electric vehicle industry.

- Most long-term owners of electric cars are so pleased with them that they plan to buy another electric car when they replace their existing model.

Living the life electric

The manufacturer of the best selling electric road car in the world is the REVA Electric Car Company. Founded in 1994, REVA is based in Bangalore – the Indian 'silicon valley' – and today have electric cars for sale in 24 countries around the world.

REVA regard themselves first and foremost as an ideas and technology company. With over 120 employees working in electric vehicle research and development and 80,000,000km of electric vehicle data collated over the past eight years, REVA have more experience of electric cars than almost any other car manufacturer.

They have recently signed a joint-venture deal with General Motors for building an electric version of the Chevrolet Spark in India, with production starting at the end of 2010.

REVA's first and best known car was simply called the REVA or REVA City and sold as the G-Wiz in the UK. Conceived and developed in the late 1990s as an urban city car, the car was originally launched in 2001 in India and 2004 in Europe. London offered additional benefits for electric car owners with exemption from the congestion charge tax levied on other car users driving in central London and offering free parking and electric charging points in many areas. This helped the car become a hit in London, with celebrities, business people, politicians and environmental enthusiasts all buying the G-Wiz in large numbers.

Cheeky, quirky and highly individualistic, G-Wiz is surprisingly fun to drive – especially the most recent models with improved safety, performance and with handling and ride tuned by Lotus – and its success has convinced major manufacturers that there is a real market for small electric city cars, with companies such as BMW, Peugeot and Honda all announcing plans for 'G-Wiz Competitors' in the next few years.

The company aspires to remain at the forefront of electric vehicle design, bringing new technology to market quicker than their competitors. Today, REVA is

developing their third generation electric cars while every other manufacturer is working on their first. The company has recently announced two new cars, the NXR sub-compact city car and the NXG two seat electric sports coupé.

The NXR will become available during 2010. It is a full four seat car with all the safety features you would expect from a mainstream manufacturer. Designed as a city car that will be primarily used as an every-day commuter car, it comfortably seats four people, has a range of 100 miles (160km) per charge and has a top speed of 65mph (104km/h).

The NXR can be charged up in 1½ hours using a fast charging station, or charged up far enough to go 25 miles (40km) in just 15 minutes. Owners can remotely monitor their car via their mobile phone, checking charge status or switching on the heating or air conditioning remotely. Optional solar roof panels can be specified, which in the right climate provides up to 1,850 miles (3,000km) of free renewable energy every year.

REVA's unique car construction design significantly reduces the production costs of its electric cars. Thanks to its electric vehicle drive train, REVA cars use around 80% fewer parts than conventional cars making them cheaper and easier to build and maintain. As a result, REVA's electric cars not only have a significantly lower carbon footprint than conventional cars, they can be sold at prices that are comparable to conventional cars: the base price for the REVA NXR City is comparable to conventional city cars built by Ford, Volkswagen and Fiat and significantly cheaper than any comparable electric car.

REVA is franchising out the assembly of their latest generation of electric cars so they can be built regionally, thereby accelerating the introduction of electric cars around the world. New factories are being built in Asia and the US. A state of the art new factory in Bangalore will be solar powered incorporating natural light, ventilation and rainwater harvesting, to ensure the carbon footprint of each car is kept as low as possible.

With electric cars being announced by almost every major manufacturer, REVA is unlikely to maintain their status as the best selling electric car manufacturer in the world for much longer.

Yet with fresh new designs, innovative technology, technical partnerships with manufacturers like General Motors, new factories being built around the world and an enviable environmental record that no major car manufacturer can match, REVA is well on their way to becoming the cleanest and coolest electric car manufacturer for the coming decade.

Go Clubbing!

Car sharing with a car club is a great option for electric car owners who just occasionally need a bigger car, or need a conventional car for occasional long distance journeys.

Over the past ten years, car sharing has gained huge momentum. If you live in a major city anywhere in the world, chances are there is a car sharing club in your area.

Above: A MINI is just one of the cars you can hire by the hour with the Zipcar car club. You can book on the internet, by phone, or using your iPhone or iPod.

Car clubs work by providing cars in designated parking slots in local areas. They are accessed using a smart card electronic key and PIN number.

Car club members can book a car for anything from half an hour upwards. The booking can be made via the internet or by telephone.

Members can elect to pay for their cars on a monthly subscription scheme, or 'pay as they go', paying an hourly rental fee for the car as and when they need it. The payment includes all fuel, insurance and maintenance costs.

The largest car sharing club is run by Zipcar, who operate 6,500 cars in over 50 cities in North America and the United Kingdom. City Car Club in the United Kingdom has over 500 cars in 15 English cities.

The secret of their success is in providing lots of vehicles across a city so that they are convenient for everyone to get to and there is always a car available.

In Chicago, for instance, Zipcar has over 400 cars in 140 locations around the city. Cars range from small compact hatchbacks to luxury cars. The success of the scheme has significantly reduced the number of cars on Chicago's streets.

It is estimated that each Zipcar replaces 15-20 personally owned cars. On average, each Zipcar member drives around 5,000 miles (8,000km) each year and saves around $450 (£300) per month by not owning a car.

"Zipcar membership in Chicago is up nearly 50% since last year," said Mark Norman, President and COO of Zipcar.

"Zipcar users report household spending on transportation of 6% versus the national average of 19%. The growing group of Zipcar members in Chicago has contributed to an estimated 10,000 fewer personally owned vehicles on Chicago's streets and more than $50 million saved by Chicago's Zipcar member households each year."

Over the next few years, car clubs and car sharing is expected to gain further momentum, with 10% of the population expected to adopt car sharing as their primary mode of transportation by 2025.

WILL AN ELECTRIC CAR WORK FOR ME?

It is important to really think about whether you are one of those people for whom an electric car is the right choice. To do this you need to consider whether it is practical in your circumstance.

Understanding whether or not an electric car is suitable for you requires you to think about how you use a car and question what is important about a car.

This process may take you some time to go through. Don't expect to have all the answers immediately. Owning an electric car is quite often a lifestyle choice and deciding whether or not an electric car is suitable for you can take some time.

Read through this chapter, consider it, then read the rest of the book. Then come back to this chapter and re-read it when you are ready. You may come up with an entirely different set of answers the second time around.

To understand whether or not an electric car will work for you, ask yourself some questions:

What benefits will I get from owning an electric car?

What benefits do you expect to get from owning an electric car?

- Lower running costs?
- Better fuel economy?
- A way of allowing you to carry out your daily driving at reduced impact on the environment?
- The opportunity to drive something different, new and interesting?

You probably already have some definite ideas about the benefits of electric cars but you may not yet know all the benefits of owning one. Reading this book should fill in some of the gaps and prompt some fresh ideas.

Take time to consider why you want to use an electric car. There will be more than one reason. Understanding all your motivations for driving an electric car will certainly help you to work out whether or not an electric car is going to be suitable for you.

Where do I live and where do I drive?

If you live in a town or city and most of your driving is in built up areas, an electric car makes a lot of sense. Almost every model of electric car on the market today will be suitable for this sort of travelling.

If you live in a small country village miles from anywhere, an electric car can make sense but you will need to choose a model that can travel at a reasonable speed. Even if you are not usually a fast driver, I would recommend choosing a car that can reach speeds of at least 50mph (80km/h) in order to comfortably keep up with other road traffic.

If you do a lot of travelling on high speed freeways for long distances, you will need to check that the electric car you choose is suitable. Range is considerably reduced at higher speeds. An electric car with an advertised range of 100 miles is not going to achieve that range if travelling at 70-80mph (112-128km/h) for long periods of time.

How far do I travel in an average day?

Some electric cars are best suited to city only driving. Others are suitable for both city driving and long distance driving.

Even if an electric car is capable of long distance driving, the characteristics of an electric vehicle mean they are more efficient and better for shorter journeys at lower speeds. Cars like the Mitsubishi i-MiEV can quite happily cruise at 70-80mph (112-128km/h) but range will be significantly reduced at these faster speeds.

You need to ascertain whether the distance you drive in a day is comfortably within the range of an electric car. If it isn't, are you able to put the car on charge between journeys?

You need to maintain a margin for error – to ensure that you have enough range on your car to comfortably carry out all your journeys.

As a general guide, you should choose an electric car with a range at least one third more than you believe you will travel between charges. If possible, you should choose an electric car with double the range than you expect to need.

For instance, if you need to travel 25 miles (40km) a day and do not have the facility to recharge the car during the day, you need to choose a car with a range of at least 38 miles (60km) and preferably 50 miles (80km).

Having this extra range means that you should comfortably be able to travel as far as you need each day, no matter what happens:

- In the winter, the range of the car will decrease by around 20-25% when the batteries are very cold.

- You are also more likely to require heating, lighting and windscreen wipers on at the same time, all of which have an impact on range.

- The range does decrease when the batteries are old. Ensuring you have more range than you need when you first buy your electric car ensures this does not become an issue.

Where can I plug in?

Do you have a garage, or at least off road parking that allows you to plug your car in to charge it up at night?

If you do, charging up your electric car is going to be easy. You may wish to install an outside power socket but in essence, you're going to have no difficulties charging up your car.

If you park in a private communal area, then you may need to seek permission from whoever manages this parking area and will almost certainly have to pay for any work to be carried out.

Often you will get an extremely co-operative response when it comes to arranging this. If you can fit a charging point to an outside wall and there is a suitable power supply at hand, then the costs can be reasonable. If, however, you need to install a freestanding charging post and run underground cables, the cost can become very significant very quickly.

If you only have on-road parking, you may not be able to charge your electric car at your house. Some electric car owners have been known to trail cables across footpaths but this is very dangerous as it poses a significant trip hazard for young children and the elderly.

I have seen one ingenious method for roadside charging where an electric car owner ran a cable from their house into a tree at the edge of the road. They then fitted a charging socket inside the tree and cleverly disguised it all to look like a birds nest!

In some countries local council offices can arrange for an electric charging point to be installed outside your house, installing a 'power bollard' by the side of the road. Costs vary dramatically and are rarely cheap, although subsidies for installing household power bollards are being considered in many countries.

Some houses with no off-road parking do have a small yard at the front of the house. These are often not large enough for a full sized car, but many compact electric cars are small enough to be parked on these yards. You can arrange for your local council to install a 'drop kerb' on the footpath next to your house and convert the front yard into a short driveway, thereby ensuring you always have a charging bay for your electric car.

Some electric car owners have made arrangements with local businesses, allowing them to charge up at the business premises outside of business hours. There are benefits for the business in allowing this:

- There is activity at their premises outside of working hours, thereby making the property less of a target for burglary and vandalism,

- It can help local business nurture goodwill and a reputation for being environmentally friendly.

Can I charge my car elsewhere?

If your place of work has a private car park, you may wish to enquire as to whether you would be allowed to charge your car at work, either by trailing a power lead through a window on an occasional basis, or having an external power socket installed for more regular use.

Even if you live well within range of your workplace, having the ability to charge your car at work can be useful from time to time.

Many towns and cities now have public charging points, with new ones becoming available all the time. Knowing the location of your nearby charging points is useful information, even if you do not plan to use them. If nothing else, knowing where they are gives you peace of mind.

Can I remove the batteries to recharge them?

I am asked this question a lot. Many people assume the size of an electric car battery would be similar in size and weight to a standard starter battery used in a conventional car.

Sadly, this is not the case. It would resolve a lot of problems if they were! The batteries required to power an electric car are bulky and heavy. Imagine a battery pack at least the size and weight of a large combustion engine. You would require heavy lifting gear to remove the whole pack in one go.

A company called Better Place have designed a battery swap out station and are working with Renault to build electric cars that are capable of having their batteries swapped out. The first of these 'Quickdrop' centres will open in Europe in the summer of 2011 at the same time the first of the Renault electric cars become available.

The unit itself is huge. It is designed to be installed in fuel service stations. It is not designed for home use.

How often do I need to be able to drive further than an electric car will allow me to go?

From time to time, most people will need to travel further than an electric car will allow them to go.

41

If you are buying an electric car as a second car, this is not a major consideration. Instead you can simply use your other car for the long distance journeys.

If you are buying an electric car as an only vehicle, there are options available to you:

- Travel by train.

- Join a car club that allows you access to a car as and when you need one and allows you to hire by the hour.

- Hire a car from a car hire company.

- Some electric car suppliers have arrangements with car hire companies to allow you to hire cars for occasional use at discounted rates.

Hiring a car for occasional use actually does make a lot of sense. It allows you to choose a suitable car for the purpose. A large car for travelling with a group of people, a small car on another occasion, even a luxury car for impressing your boss!

Sharing a car with a car club can cost as little as £3.50 per hour in the UK, or $4.50 per hour in the United States. The cost includes all fuel costs and insurance. A full day's car rental can cost as little as £19 in the UK, or $25 in the United States.

If you are regularly going to be travelling further than an electric car will allow you to go and you do not have access to another car, are you going to be happy to use public transport? Is this going to be practical? Regularly commuting from one city to another by train may be a practical option for some people but may be completely implausible for others.

What if an electric car is not suitable for me now?

This is a good point to take stock. If you have already decided against an electric car then that is a shame but at least you have vital information. It is better than spending thousands on a car before discovering that an electric car is not suitable.

Electric cars are continuing to evolve and improve. Even if an electric car is not a practical solution now, they may well be in two or three year's time.

There two other options that you may wish to consider:

Sharing a car

Do you live close to friends or family that would also be interested in owning an electric car? If so, why not pool resources and buy an electric car between you? If you then share all the cars you have, you can then use an electric car for shorter journeys and another car for long distance driving.

Sharing cars seems a difficult concept to accept for many. For many people in their thirties and over, the car has been seen as a symbol of freedom – of escape. Everyone from my generation can remember their first car and how they were able to use it to escape from parents and parental control.

Young people do not associate freedom with escape. To them, freedom means keeping in touch with friends via Facebook, MySpace and mobile phone, or playing computer games with their friends.

To young people, freedom means sharing. Research shows that young people are far more open to the concept of sharing cars, in the same way they share video games[2].

The concept of pooling cars and sharing them between friends and family may seem alien today but is likely to become commonplace in just a few years time.

Zipcar, one of the largest car clubs in the world, believe that 10% of the population in the US will adopt car sharing by 2025.

Change your life!

This might sound a rather drastic title but many people who are looking to buy an electric car are doing so as part of a much larger life changing transition. It is not uncommon for people to buy electric cars having recently changed jobs, retired or moved house, as part of a bigger plan to improve their lives.

Your dream life may consist of living in a cave in the side of a hillside, living in the latest ultra-high tech eco home, or just living a

---

[2] Which World is Real? The future of virtual reality – Science Clarified.

simpler life. Whatever it is, learn how you can reduce your dependence on your existing car first. Don't try to live your life with an electric car before you are ready.

Chapter Summary

- For some people, an electric car is the perfect choice for them. For others, they are impractical for the time being.

- You need to consider how you use a car.

- Owning an electric car is often a lifestyle choice. Don't hurry the process.

- There are a few practical points you need to consider:
    - Where you live and how far you travel.
    - Where you can plug in to recharge.
    - How often you need to travel beyond the range of an electric car and how you plan to do that.

PURCHASING AND RUNNING COSTS

In general, electric cars are more expensive to purchase than comparable combustion engine cars.

There are a few notable exceptions to this rule as we will see later. In general, however, electric cars have a cost premium of at least 25% over other cars.

This additional cost can be offset by the higher resale value of many electric cars and by tax offsets and other financial incentives offered in many countries.

Leasing schemes

Some manufacturers are only providing their electric cars on leasing schemes as opposed to outright purchase.

Mitsubishi, MINI and Smart for example, are offering their cars on fixed term leases, after which time the cars will be returned to the manufacturers.

The leasing cost for these cars is often higher than the leasing cost for an equivalent combustion engine car. However, almost all of these leasing schemes incorporate servicing, warranty and vehicle breakdown and in some cases insurance. Remember, you are also not paying for fuel from a filling station.

All this helps offset the difference in cost.

Fuel Costs

The biggest single cost saving with an electric car is a reduction in fuel costs.

Instead of paying for fuel at a filling station, an electric car owner simply plugs a cable into the car overnight and charges up using off-peak electricity.

From empty to full, most electric cars use between 8 and 20kWh (1 kWh = 1 unit of electricity on your utility bill) to provide a complete charge. In the UK, off-peak electricity typically costs around 6–8 pence per kWh. In the United States off-peak electricity costs around 4–6 cents.

Here's an example: If an electric car driver travels around 30 miles (48km) a day, that equates to around 900 miles (1440km) a month.

The car can be charged using off-peak electricity. 30 miles of driving with an electric car like the MINI E, Mitsubishi i-MiEV, Aixam City or the REVA *i* would equate to around 6kWh of power.

Cost Savings in the United Kingdom

In the UK, based on 6 pence a unit cost, the cost of recharging the car would be 36 pence a night, just under £11 a month.

Compared to a conventional car that gives 35mpg (7.7km per litre, based on the imperial gallon), you're using roughly 136 litres of petrol per month to go the same distance. At a cost of £1.05 a litre, that is a total cost of £142 per month.

Based on these calculations, the cost of charging an electric car is less than 8% of the cost of putting fuel into a conventional car.

Cost Savings in the United States

In the US, based on 4 cents a unit cost, the cost of charging the same car would be 24 cents a night, just over $7 a month.

Compared to a conventional car that gives 30mpg, you're using roughly 35 gallons of petrol per month to go the same distance. At a cost of $2.60 per US gallon, that is a total cost of $91 a month.

Based on these calculations, the cost of charging an electric car is 8½% of the cost of putting fuel into a conventional car.

The sting in the tail

Unfortunately, it would be wrong to show purely the recharging costs as the full running costs for running an electric car. There is an additional cost to be taken into account when you are charging up an electric car: the cost of the batteries.

Electric car batteries do not last forever. They lose capacity over time and eventually have to be replaced.

Unfortunately these replacement costs can be very high. Prices start from around £1,000 in the UK or $1,600 in the US for a basic electric car and rise to several thousand for a more powerful car.

If these battery replacement costs are amortized over a period of several years, offset against the cost of fuel in a combustion engine car, the overall cost is still cheaper than visiting a filling station and paying for fuel every week. Unfortunately, because the battery replacement costs are so high, it can be a painful experience when they need to be replaced!

Purchasing or leasing batteries?

To take away this sting, many electric car manufacturers allow you to lease the batteries from them rather than buy them. It is then the responsibility of the manufacturer to replace batteries as and when they come to their end of their natural life.

As the battery is leased over a period of several years, the monthly leasing cost is low, which means that even when battery costs are added to recharging costs, an electric car is very cheap to run.

Of course, over the long term it is still cheaper to buy the batteries outright and then pay for them to be replaced as and when required.

Despite that, leasing offers the very significant benefit that there are no large bills to be paid come battery replacement time and means a reduced capital cost on the purchase of the car with batteries.

Ultimately whether you choose to buy or lease the batteries is a personal choice. Most manufacturers who offer battery leasing will also allow you to buy the batteries with the car should you prefer to.

Electric car purchasing plans

A number of electric car manufacturers and distributors are looking at different economic models for selling their cars in the future. One model that looks particularly interesting is referred to as the 'cell phone' model.

For years, cell phones have been provided as part of a talk plan. The cost of the cell phones is reduced based on the number of calls you make.

A similar concept is being promoted for electric car use. In this business model, the purchase cost of the car is reduced and you pay a recharging fee every time you plug in the car to charge up. The recharging fee covers the cost of the electricity, the cost of the batteries and all the servicing costs for the car. This means you never get hit with a big maintenance bill with your car, you simply pay as you use.

Servicing Costs

One benefit that has been claimed for electric cars is lower servicing costs. After all, fewer parts equate to simpler maintenance, so in theory servicing an electric car should cost less than a car with a combustion engine.

This is true to a point. If you want to service your electric car yourself, the chances are it will be cheaper than servicing any other vehicle. Many people who have older electric cars do the servicing themselves and have saved themselves money as a result. This is especially true at battery replacement time.

If you want to have your car serviced by an electric vehicle dealer, you pay more for the specialist skills. Inevitably, this means the overall servicing costs for an electric car are about the same as for other cars.

It is worth pointing out that some electric vehicle dealers do charge excessively for replacement batteries. If you are buying the batteries rather than leasing them, you need to be prepared to shop around at battery replacement time in order to get the best value for money.

Resale Values

Electric car resale values have traditionally been extremely high as demand for the cars has outstripped supply. When the G-Wiz electric car first appeared in London, demand was so high that the car had the lowest depreciation of any new car in the UK, outperforming traditionally low-depreciating brands such as Mercedes and Audi.

In the United States, used electric cars generally sell at significant premiums over their conventional engine equivalents. In the United States a 1999 Ford Ranger EV was recently sold on eBay for $15,000. A 1993 Geo Metro converted to electric power sold for $5,000.

By and large, that scenario still exists. Overall, electric cars command good resale values. The one exception is London where the G-Wiz has become so plentiful residual values for all makes and models of small electric cars in London have suffered. Similarly, in the southern states of America, the neighborhood electric vehicle (NEV) cars are comparatively cheap to buy on the used market.

This makes them excellent value for money and in both cases cars are often distributed to other parts of the country where their rarity ensures they command better prices.

Chapter Summary

- In general, electric cars are more expensive to purchase than other cars at the moment, although there are exceptions.

- Charging an electric car is very cheap but to get a true cost of using an electric car, you should factor in the battery leasing costs or a percentage of the cost for replacing the batteries.

- To avoid a hefty battery replacement bill, it is preferable to lease the batteries rather than buy them outright.

- Servicing costs are comparable with other cars.

- Resale values for electric cars are generally very good.

Creating the national charging network

Tim Nicklin is the founder of the EV Network, a UK not-for-profit body that is building up a network of electric car charging points throughout the United Kingdom, with individual electric car owners sharing their own personal charging points with others.

Tell me about the EV Network

The EV Network is a UK-wide database showing where electric vehicle charge points can be found – public charge points, those provided by companies for their visitors and those shared by members on an exchange basis.

Why did you decide to start up the network?

I'd taken delivery of my own electric vehicle in early 2007 and, as I started to travel further from home, was looking for places where I could recharge. However I found was there wasn't a single website with all the information available and so decided to share what I was gathering with others.

How does the network make money?

In short it doesn't. At the moment it's funded from my own pocket.

As the network grows we will need more administrative support, so in time it might become grant-funded or a subscription service in order to cover the operating costs.

How important is it for electric car owners to have a charging network?

If electric cars are ever to replace significant numbers of conventional vehicles then a network will be necessary to break the ties of only being able to operate in a limited area around home or work. Personally I think that most EV users mostly will charge at their homes but for longer trips a network will be necessary.

The existence of a network will also help users gain confidence in using their vehicles. Even if you don't actually need to use the facilities, it's always reassuring to know that they are there.

How many charging points are there across the UK now?

Currently there are around 400 charging points in public locations plus others offered by EV Network members.

What are your plans and aspirations for the EV Network in the future?

I should like to see the EV Network seen as the national database for EV charging locations and to make a significant contribution towards increasing the numbers of EVs in the UK.

However my ultimate measure of success is when it's no longer required - that is when you can drive anywhere in the UK and be confident of being able to find facilities to charge your vehicle.

What about the rest of the world?

Around 30% of visitors to the EV Network website come from outside the UK, from a total of almost eighty countries.

Non-UK visitors mostly come from the USA, elsewhere in Europe, the Far East and Australasia.

What advice would you give to anyone considering setting up a similar project in other countries?

I've had discussions with various parties overseas interested in doing the same in their own countries, either seeking advice to do their own thing, or contracting with the EV Network to replicate the site for another geographic area.

It's great to have the support of relevant enthusiast groups. Many of our members come from the REVA/G-Wiz Owners Club and the Battery Vehicle Society.

www.EV-Network.org.uk

ELECTRIC CARS YOU CAN DRIVE TODAY

The electric car industry is still young and full of potential but there is a myth abroad that electric cars are not easily available.

Both new and used electric cars are available from a number of manufacturers. Some of the new cars from mainstream manufacturers are only available on lease plans, or only in certain locations. Other manufacturers and distributors have made sure that electric cars are available to purchase around the world.

Most of the cars listed in this chapter are available right now but there are a few that are not available at time of writing but that are scheduled for production during 2010.

Categories of electric car

There are a number of different categories of electric car around. The categories are NEVs, quadricycles, tricycles and cars. Here is a brief description of each category of vehicle:

Cars

Figure 2 - the REVA NXR sub-compact city car

Cars are the mainstream vehicles here. They are capable of reasonable performance and most importantly, for our definition, have been subjected to stringent safety regulations in their design and build, incorporating air bags and properly designed and tested crush zones.

All cars have been subjected to crash testing[3] and have had to pass a number of checks and tests in order to be certified roadworthy.

Figure 3 – The Renault Fluence ZE electric car goes on sale in Europe in September 2010, with first customer deliveries expected in Summer 2011.

All of the new electric vehicles designs being developed by mainstream vehicle manufacturers (with the exception of Chrysler's GEM and Peapod divisions) are technically classed as cars.

NEV's

In the United States, there is a class of low-speed electric vehicles classified as Neighborhood Electric Vehicles (NEVs). NEVs are lightweight vehicles designed for city use only.

---

[3]In Europe, very small manufacturers who are building less than fifty vehicles each year can avoid crash testing through a Single Vehicle Approval scheme where each car has to be individually inspected to ensure the car can be certified roadworthy.

In the past, NEVs were restricted to a top speed of 25mph (40km/h) and could only be driven on roads with a speed limit of 35mph or less. This meant that NEVs were extremely restricted in use and were best suited to gated communities, campuses, large parks, estates and central city areas.

Several states have now updated their legislation; creating a new class of 'Medium Speed Vehicle' which means many NEVs are now allowed to travel at speeds of up to 35mph (56km/h) and can travel on roads with speed limits of up to 45mph. At time of writing, Minnesota, Oklahoma, Montana, Washington, Kentucky and Tennessee have passed these laws with many other States currently considering them.

By reducing these restrictions, NEVs are now a practical option for millions of Americans who live and work in major cities and predominantly use their cars for short journeys around town.

Figure 4 - the Peapod neighborhood electric vehicle

Small commercial NEVs, mainly trucks and small vans, have become popular with some local authorities where they are often used for street cleaning, park management and refuse collection in central city areas. The American Army also uses thousands of

NEVs as small personnel carriers, for deliveries and for maintenance duties around military bases.

NEVs are not subject to the same safety regulations as normal cars because of their restricted speed.

As you are looking through the list of vehicles on the following pages, you will notice that all NEVs are shown as having a top speed of 25mph. In most cases, the cars have been electronically restricted to this speed.

In the American States that allow an NEV to travel at 35mph, the top speed of the vehicle can normally be increased by the dealer.

Low Speed Vehicles (LSV)

Canada used to have a Low Speed Vehicles legislation that was similar to the United States original NEV legislation. However, this was not popular with many states and the legislation was rescinded during 2008, restricting LSVs to gated communities.

As a consequence, no new LSV vehicles are available in Canada. Existing vehicles built before the law was changed can still be used on the roads.

Quadricycles

The European equivalent to NEVs is the quadricycles category. Unlike NEVs, most quadricycles are not speed restricted and can be driven on any road. They are, however, power restricted which means that most have a typical top speed of 40–50mph (65–80km/h).

Diesel powered quadricycles have been on sale in Europe since the early 1980s, whilst electric quadricycles have appeared in the past few years. There are over 300,000 quadricycles on the roads across Western European.

Like NEVs, quadricycles are not subject to the same safety regulations as normal cars and do not have to be subjected to crash testing. Despite this, many manufacturers voluntarily submit their quadricycles to crash testing in order to maintain customer confidence.

Figure 5 - the Aixam Mega City quadricycle

In France, Europe's largest market for quadricycles, they are three times less likely to be involved in an accident than a conventional car[4]. Accidents with quadricycles are two times less likely to result in serious injuries than accidents with cars.[5]

Tricycles

In both North America and Europe, three wheeled vehicles under a certain weight limit are technically classed as motorcycles and not cars. In most countries, this means that they can be driven by motorcycle riders (although restrictions exist in some cases).

Like NEVs and quadricycles, this means they are not subject to the same safety regulations as normal cars.

Unlike NEVs and quadricycles, most tricycles do not have power or speed restrictions and can be legally driven on any road.

---

[4]The French National Interministerial Road Safety Observatory.

[5]European Quadricycle Manufacturers and Importers Association.

Figure 6 - Above: Aptera 2e Below: the Myers DUO

Most of the electric tricycles currently being launched in the United States are very far from the image most people have for tricycles. They are fast, sleek, high tech vehicles like the Aptera, the Triac and the Duo. These vehicles all offer rapid performance and excellent range, combining efficient aerodynamics and light weight.

Light Quadricycles/Restricted Tricycles

In Europe, there is another category of vehicle known as a light quadricycle. These vehicles are power and speed restricted with a top speed of 28mph (40km/h). In Europe, these can be driven by 16 year olds who are otherwise restricted to riding small mopeds.

Electric vehicles you can buy today:

Make/Model	Vehicle Class	Available New (as of April 2010)	Available Used	To be launched in 2010	Countries or Regions
Aixam Mega City	Quad	Yes	Yes		Across Europe
AEV Kurrent	NEV	Yes	Yes		US
Aptera 2e	Tricycle	No	No	Spring	California
BYD e6	Car	Yes	No	Yes	China, US in 2010
Citroen Berlingo	Car	No	Yes	No	Europe
Citroen Saxo	Car	No	Yes		Europe
Citroen C-Zero	Car	No	No	End 2010	Europe
Chevrolet e-Spark	Car	No	No	End 2010	India
Coda Sedan	Car	No	No	Yes	US
CommuterCars Tango	Car	Yes	Yes	No	North America
Dynasty IT	NEV	Yes	Yes		US and Pakistan
ECC Citroen C1	Car	Yes	No		UK
Effedi Maranello 4Cycle	Quad	Yes	Yes		Europe
Elcat Citywagon 202	Car	No	Yes		UK and Finland
Estrima Biro	Light Quad	Yes	No		Europe
Ford Ranger EV	Car	No	Yes		North America
Ford Tourneo	Car	No	No	Summer	North America
GEM e2/e4/e6	NEV/ Quad	Yes	Yes		US and Europe
Green Vehicles Triac	Tricycle	No	No	Spring	North America
Kandi Coco	NEV	Yes	No		Oklahoma, US

Make/Model	Vehicle Class	Available New (as of April 2010)	Available Used	To be launched in 2010	Countries or Regions
Kewet El-Jet	Car	No	Yes		Nordic
Kewet Buddy	Car	No	Yes		Northern Europe
Kewet METRObuddy	Car	Yes	No	Spring	Northern Europe
Liberty Electric Range Rover	Car	Yes	No		UK
Miles ZX40S	NEV	Yes	Yes		US
MINI e	Car	Yes - Rental	No		Trials in US & UK
Mitsubishi iMiEV	Car	Yes - Rental	No		Japan and UK
MyCar	Quad	Yes	Yes		UK, Hong Kong
Myers NMG	Tricycle	Yes	Yes		US
Myers Duo	Tricycle	No	No	Summer	US
Nissan Leaf	Car	No	No	Fall	US
Peapod	NEV	No	No	Spring	US
Peugeot 106 Electrique	Car	No	Yes		Europe
Phoenix SUT	Car	No	No	Spring	US
Phoenix SUV	Car	No	No	Spring	US
Renault Clio Electro	Car	No	Yes		France
Renault Fluence	Car	No	No	Sept	Europe
Renault Twizy	Car	No	No	Sept	Europe
REVA / G-Wiz dc-drive	Quad	No	Yes		UK, India
REVA / G-Wiz ac-drive	Quad	No	Yes		Europe, Asia, S. America
REVA i / G-Wiz i	Quad	Yes	Yes		Europe, Asia, S. America

Make/Model	Vehicle Class	Available New (as of April 2010)	Available Used	To be launched in 2010	Countries or Regions
REVA L-ion / G-Wiz L-ion	Quad	Yes	No		Europe, Asia, South America
REVA NXR	Car	No	No	Fall	Worldwide
Mercedes Smart ForTwo	Car	No	No	Rental - Summer	Parts of UK
Start Lab Street	Quad	Yes	Yes		Europe
Start Lab Allroad	Quad	Yes	Yes		Europe
Stevens ZeCar	Car	Yes	No		UK
SunMotor DX	NEV	Yes	No		US
Tata Indica Vista EV	Car	No	No	Rental – Summer	Parts of UK
Tazzari	Quad	Yes	No		Europe
Tesla	Car	Yes	No		US and UK
TH!NK City Mk1	Car	No	Yes		Norway
TH!NK Neighbor	NEV	No	Yes		California
TH!NK City Mk2	Car	No	No	Spring	Europe and US
Toyota RAV4	Car	No	Yes		US and UK
Twike	Tricycle	Yes	Yes		Europe
Venturi Fetish	Car	Yes	Yes		Europe
Venturi Eclectic	Quad	No	No	Spring	Europe
Wheego Whip	NEV	Yes	No		US
Wheego Whip 2	Car	No	No	Summer	US
ZAP! Xebra	Tricycle	Yes	Yes		North America
Zenn	NEV	Yes	Yes		US

Aixam

Aixam are a French manufacturer and are the leading manufacturer of quadricycles in the world. They manufacture around 15,000 vehicles a year which are sold throughout Europe.

The Aixam Mega City has a range of around 40–50 miles (65–80km). It is a common sight in France and The Netherlands and has gained popularity in the United Kingdom, especially in and around London.

Aixam have one of the largest dealers and servicing networks of any electric car manufacturer in Europe, with 130 dealers in France and over 300 servicing agents in the United Kingdom.

As well as a small quadricycle, Aixam sell a range of small electric commercial vans and trucks.

Mega City Mk 1

Body Styles:	2 door/2 seat hatchback
Top Speed:	40mph / 65km/h
Range:	40 miles / 65km
Recharge Time:	8 hours
Economy:	10km/kWh
Availability:	Used only across Europe
Comments:	Built between 2006-2008 and available as a two seater or 2+2, sold as the NICE CITY in the UK

Mega City Mk 2

Body Styles:	2 door/4 seat hatchback
Top Speed:	40mph / 65km/h
Range:	40 miles / 65km
Recharge Time:	8 hours
Economy:	9km/kWh
Availability:	New across Europe
Comments:	An updated Mega City with fresh styling, improved ergonomics and interior and seating for four.

American Electric Vehicle

The American Electric Vehicle Company (AEVC) builds and sells the Kurrent neighborhood electric vehicle.

The Kurrent is an Italian designed two seat car (where it is sold as the Start Lab Open). The Kurrent has been modified specifically for the US market and sells as an NEV.

Body Styles:	2 seat coupe
Top Speed:	25mph / 40km/h
Range:	30 miles / 45km
Recharge Time:	8 hours
Economy:	9km/kWh
Availability:	United States
Comments:	Also available with a longer wheelbase as a truck and light van.

Aptera

Is it a car? Is it a plane? Is it a UFO? No, it's an Aptera!

With jaw-dropping looks that look like the car is out of the pages of a sci-fi novel, the Aptera seats two people, provides highway performance and a range of 100 miles (160km).

The Aptera is a three wheel car, which makes it technically classed as a motorbike. Its aerodynamic shape ensures superb range and performance.

First cars will be delivered to their customers in early 2010. First cars will be available in California only and over 4,000 people have put their names down on the waiting list.

Aptera 2e

Body Styles:	2 seat alien landing craft
Top Speed:	Est. 85mph / 137km/h
Range:	100 miles / 160km
Recharge Time:	Unknown
Economy:	9km/kWh
Availability:	New – California only – early 2010.

BYD

BYD are a Chinese rechargeable battery manufacturer that opened an electric car division in 2003.

Their first cars are now in production and are selling in China. North American sales are scheduled to commence in 2010.

E6

Body Styles:	MPV
Top Speed:	100mph / 160km/h
Range:	Up to 249 miles / 400km (depending on battery chosen)
Recharge Time:	Unknown
Economy:	6km/kWh
Availability:	China – now; North America – 2010.

Citroen

Citroen were one of the pioneers in bringing electric cars back to our roads when in the late 1990s they launched electric versions of the Citroen Saxo city car and the Citroen Berlingo.

Unfortunately, they were not a success owing to their very high purchase price. The models were quietly withdrawn, just before the current momentum for electric vehicles started. Second hand values are strong and there are specialists who can maintain them.

Citroen return to the electric car market at the end of 2010 with a small five door hatchback – the Citroen C-Zero.

Citroen Berlingo

Body Styles:	Estate car/van
Top Speed:	55mph / 88km/h
Range:	60 miles / 98km
Recharge Time:	8 hours
Economy:	Not Known
Availability:	Used only – across Europe

Citroen Saxo

Body Styles:	3 and 5 door hatchback
Top Speed:	50mph / 80km/h
Range:	40 miles / 65km
Recharge Time:	8 hours
Economy:	Not Known
Availability:	Used only – across Europe
Comments:	Built in small numbers between 1999 and 2003 and now only available second hand.

Citroen C-Zero

Body Styles:	5 door hatchback
Top Speed:	81mph / 129km/h
Range:	80 miles / 128km
Recharge Time:	6 hours
Economy:	10km/kWh
Availability:	Late 2010 – across Europe
Comments:	A rebranded Mitsubishi iMiEV

Chevrolet India

Whilst all eyes are on Chevrolet in the US with their new Volt hybrid car, Chevrolet India has been quietly developing a new entirely electric five door supermini – the e-Spark.

Developed in conjunction with electric car specialists, REVA, the car goes on sale in India in October 2010. It is likely to be the cheapest five door electric car in the world.

Body Styles:	5 door hatchback
Top Speed:	Not Known
Range:	Not Known
Recharge Time:	8 hours
Economy:	Not Known
Availability:	Late 2010 in India.

Coda Automotive

Coda Automotive are a new manufacturer developing a new four door electric sedan for the North American market.

The first 200 cars will be made available during 2010 with volume production becoming available early in 2011.

Coda Sedan

Body Styles:	4 door hatchback
Top Speed:	80mph / 128km
Range:	120 miles / 192km
Recharge Time:	6 hours
Economy:	Not Known
Availability:	Limited availability during 2010 in United States only.
Comments:	Eight year battery warranty

CommuterCars

CommuterCars are an American company based in Washington State. Their car, the Tango, is a narrow-bodied two seat car with rapid performance and tandem seating.

The cars are currently supplied in kit form. Full production is planned at some stage in the future.

The Tango is very rapid: 0-60mph (0-100km/h) takes under 4 seconds and the top speed is reputed to be 150mph (240km/h), making this the fastest electric car today.

Tango T600

Body Styles:	Two seat tandem
Top Speed:	150mph / 240km/h
Range:	80 miles / 130km
Recharge Time:	6 hours
Economy:	Not Known
Availability:	Across the United States

Dynasty

Originally a Canadian company, Dynasty cars are now built in Pakistan and sold in the United States. Classed as an NEV, it is a small, practical five door hatchback. A van is also available.

A few vehicles were brought to the United Kingdom in 2006 where they were sold as quadricycles, tuned with a higher top speed of 40mph (65km/h) but were never actively marketed.

IT

Body Styles:	Four door, four seat hatchback and van
Top Speed:	25mph / 40km/h
Range:	40 miles / 65km
Recharge Time:	6 hours
Economy:	Not Known
Availability:	United States, Pakistan.

Effedi

Effedi are the Italian manufacturer of a small electric two seat quadricycle called the Maranello 4Cycle.

Currently only available in Italy, Spain and Norway, the vehicle has been previously sold in the United Kingdom and the United States and a few used examples occasionally come up for sale.

Maranello 4Cycle

Body Styles:	Two seat hatchback
Top Speed:	30mph / 45km/h
Range:	40 miles / 65km
Recharge Time:	6 hours
Economy:	10km/kWh
Availability:	New: Italy, Spain, Norway. Used: United Kingdom, United States.

Electric Car Corporation

Electric Car Corporation (ECC) produces a conversion on the popular Citroen C1 super-mini. Called the C1 Evie, the car is supported through the UK Citroen dealer network and is supplied through the Electric Car Corporation (ECC).

Citroen C1 Evie

Body Styles:	3 and 5 door hatchback
Top Speed:	60mph / 98km
Range:	70 miles / 112km
Recharge Time:	6 hours
Economy:	Not Known
Availability:	New – Currently United Kingdom only

Estrima

Estrima are a new company with a new light quadricycle called the Birò. Launched in late 2009 and only available in Italy, the company is looking to sell its car across Europe and in the United States in 2010.

The company is selling the vehicle as a practical alternative to a small motorbike and in Europe it can be driven by 16 year olds who are otherwise restricted to riding small mopeds.

Birò

Body Styles:	Open coupe
Top Speed:	30mph / 45km/h
Range:	40 miles / 60km
Recharge Time:	8 hours
Economy:	10km/kWh
Availability:	Currently only Italy –Europe and US planned in 2010

Ford

Ford invested heavily in electric vehicles in the late 1990s, purchasing Norwegian electric car manufacturer TH!NK and producing an electric version of their Ranger pickup truck.

Ford will be the first of the 'Detroit Three' to launch a range of electric cars with the first vehicles available in 2010.

A derivative of their first vehicle, the Transit Connect BEV, is already available in the UK, Ireland and The Netherlands, where it is sold as the Smiths Ampere.

Available as a van (Transit Connect) or car (Tourneo), the car is capable of travelling at speeds of up to 70mph (112km/h) and has a range of up to 100 miles (160km).

In Europe, the Tourneo and Transit Connect will continue to be sold by Smiths Electric Vehicles and will only be available through Smiths distributors.

Ranger EV

Body Styles:	Pickup Truck
Top Speed:	65mph / 104km/h
Range:	65 miles / 104km
Recharge Time:	8 hours
Economy:	Not Known

1998 FORD RANGER

Availability:	Used only – in North America, few imports into Europe and Iceland.
Comments:	Built between 1998 and 2002, only available second hand.

Tourneo/Transit Connect BEV

Body Styles:	Estate car/van
Top Speed:	70mph / 112km/h
Range:	100 miles / 160km
Recharge Time:	8 hours
Economy:	Not Known
Availability:	New – UK/Ireland, US and Canada – early 2010

G-Wiz

G-Wiz is the brand name adopted for the previous model REVA in the United Kingdom. For more information, see *REVA*.

GEM

GEM (Green Eco Mobility) is a wholly owned subsidiary of Chrysler. They have been building electric vehicles for the past 12 years and are the largest manufacturer of NEVs in the United States.

Over 38,000 have been sold, mainly for use in large parks and estates, in gated communities or in central city areas.

These are technically classified as NEVs in North America and are also sold in Europe as quadricycles where they are popular with postal services, local government and for large parks and estates.

GEM vehicles are available with two seat, four seat and six seat configurations as well as light van and truck variants.

E2

Body Styles:	2 seat coupe
Top Speed:	30mph/45km/h (limited to 25mph in USA)
Range:	30 miles / 45km
Recharge Time:	8 hours
Economy:	10km/kWh
Availability:	Europe and North America

Comments:	Optional doors and various luggage options available. Also available with a longer wheelbase as a truck and light van.

E4

Body Styles:	4 seat coupe
Top Speed:	30mph/45km/h (limited to 25mph in USA)
Range:	30 miles / 45km
Recharge Time:	8 hours
Economy:	10km/kWh

Availability:	Europe and North America
Comments:	Optional doors and various luggage options available.

Green Vehicles

Green Vehicles are launching a three wheel, two seat sports car called the Triac. The car is due on the market early in 2010 and will be sold across the United States.

Triac

Body Styles:	2 seat sports car
Top Speed:	80mph / 130km/h
Range:	100 miles / 160km
Recharge Time:	6 hours
Economy::	Not Known
Availability:	North America

Kandi

Kandi import a small two seat open top NEV electric vehicle into Oklahoma, United States.

For a few happy months at the end of 2009, Oklahomans could buy their car for an incredible $865, thanks to a combination of Federal and State tax credits.

Kandi Coco

Body Styles:	2 seat convertible
Top Speed:	25mph / 40km/h
Range:	60 miles / 96km
Recharge Time:	7 hours
Economy:	Not Known
Availability:	New – Oklahoma

Kewet

Kewet are a Norwegian car manufacturer who has been building small electric city cars for many, many years.

The cars are three seat cars where the driver and two passengers sit three abreast. They are popular in Norway, Sweden and Denmark and are planning to expand into other markets during 2010, including North America, with the launch of their latest model, the METRObuddy.

El-Jet

Body Styles:	3 seat city car
Top Speed:	50mph / 80km/h
Range:	30 miles / 45km
Recharge Time:	Not Known
Economy:	Not Known
Availability:	Manufactured in the early to mid 1990s, around 200 of these cars were built. They occasionally appear on the second hand market, mainly in Norway, Germany, Sweden, Finland and Denmark.

Buddy

Body Styles:	3 seat city car
Top Speed:	60mph / 98km/h
Range:	40 miles / 60km
Recharge Time:	Not Known
Economy:	Not Known
Availability:	An updated version of the original El-Jet and sold in small numbers up until the end of 2009.

METRObuddy

Body Styles:	3 seat city car
Top Speed:	60mph / 98km/h
Range:	50 miles / 80km 75 miles / 120km
Recharge Time:	Not Known
Economy:	Not Known
Availability:	The first cars are now reaching customers in Norway and sales into other countries will start during 2010.

Liberty

Liberty Electric Cars produce a high performance electric version of the iconic Range Rover.

0–60mph (0–100km/h) is claimed to take around six seconds and the range is around 200 miles (320km).

Liberty Electric Range Rover

Body Styles:	5 door SUV
Top Speed:	100mph / 160km/h
Range:	200 miles / 320km
Recharge Time:	6 hours
Economy:	Not Known
Availability:	United Kingdom

Miles

Miles Automotive produce one of the most practical NEVs currently available in the United States. Their car is a spacious, five door hatchback with ample space for four people and their luggage.

Miles also produce a van, minibus and small truck to complete their range of electric vehicles.

ZX40S

Body Styles:	5 door hatchback
Top Speed:	25mph / 40km/h
Range:	40 miles / 65km
Recharge Time:	8 hours
Economy:	Not Known
Availability:	United States

MINI

A small number of electric MINIs are currently on lease to drivers in California and parts of the United Kingdom and Germany.

The MINI E is a two seat car. The batteries take the place where the rear seats usually are. It is promoted as a sporty electric car with rapid acceleration. 0–62mph (0–100km/h) takes around 8½ seconds and the car has a top speed of 95mph (150km/h).

The MINI E is unlikely to become a mainstream MINI model for some time to come. It is an evaluation car that will be returned to MINI when the trials are complete. MINI has not said when a mass produced electric MINI will be available.

MINI E

Body Styles:	2 door/2 seat hatchback
Top Speed:	95mph / 150km/h
Range:	120 miles (195km)
Recharge Time:	6 hours
Economy:	7km/kWh
Availability:	New – California, Southern England, Germany
Comments:	Short term lease only, no rear seats, fun to drive with good range and rapid acceleration

Mitsubishi

Mitsubishi have been developing a range of electric city cars, the first of which is now just becoming available.

This car is an adaptation of the Mitsubishi i combustion engine car that has been available for three years in Japan and the United Kingdom.

The electric version is called the i-MiEV and has recently been launched in Japan and the United Kingdom. Worldwide sales commence during the latter part of 2010.

People who have driven both the i and the i-MiEV say the electric variant is significantly better than the combustion engine version, with better performance, handling and power delivery.

Initially, the i-MiEV is only available on lease and only in small numbers. However, Mitsubishi have high ambitions for the car with plans to produce 20,000 cars a year. The i-MiEV will be joined by a two door sports coupe in 2011 and the company has also shown a small van variant.

Mitsubishi have also signed an agreement with Peugeot and Citroen that will mean both Peugeot and Citroen will be producing their own derivatives of the i-MiEV in late 2010.

Meanwhile, Mitsubishi is continuing to develop their range of electric vehicles and recently showed an electric sports car and a minivan. Sources say these will be available to the public in 2011.

i-MiEV

Body Styles:	5 door/4 seat hatchback
Top Speed:	81mph / 130km/h
Range:	100 miles (160km)
Recharge Time:	6 hours
Economy:	10km/kWh
Availability:	New – UK, Japan – now, rest of the world at the end of 2010
Comments:	Compact but with lots of internal space. Futuristic styling and excellent quality but not cheap.

MyCar

MyCar is a small, quirky, cute looking two seat electric quadricycle with the emphasis on fun.

Sold in the United Kingdom and China, the MyCar is an electric alternative to a Smart ForTwo at a comparable price.

MyCar

Body Styles:	2 door/2 seat coupe
Top Speed:	40mph / 65km/h
Range:	60 miles (98km)
Recharge Time:	5 hours
Economy:	11km/kWh
Availability:	New – UK, China
Comments:	Fun city car for the young and the young at heart.

Myers

Myers are best known for their single seat NmG (No More Gas) electric three wheeled car, previously sold as the Corbyn Sparrow.

The NmG is promoted as an all-weather alternative to a motorcycle, with a top speed of 75mph (120km/h) and a range of 45 miles (70km).

A new tricycle, called the Duo, with sleek styling and capable of seating two people will be available in mid-2010. The top speed is 75mph (120km/h) and the vehicle has a range of 60 miles (100km) or 100 miles (160km) depending on the version chosen.

NMG

Body Styles:	2 door/1 seat coupe
Top Speed:	75mph / 120km/h
Range:	45 miles (70km)
Recharge Time:	8-10 hours @ 110v 2-3 hours @ 220v
Economy:	Not Known
Availability:	New – North America
Comments:	A fun, single seat all weather alternative to a motorbike

DUO

Body Styles:	2 door/2 seat coupe
Top Speed:	75mph / 120km/h
Range:	60 miles / 100km 100 miles / 160km
Recharge Time:	Unknown
Economy	Not Known
Availability:	New – North America during 2010

Nissan

During 2010, the first North American buyers will be able to buy the Nissan Leaf. The Leaf is a family sized electric car with a 100 mile (160km range) and a top speed of 85mph (136km/h).

The first 1,000 American customers will be able to take delivery of their cars in the second half of 2010 with the first mass produced cars appearing in early 2011.

Nissan's confidence in the Leaf is such that they will not launch a combustion engine version of this car.

The Leaf will be the first new all-electric car from a mainstream manufacturer that will be available in the United States. European customers will have to wait until 2011 before they have a chance to buy one.

Nissan Leaf

Body Styles:	5 door/5 seat hatchback
Top Speed:	85mph / 136km/h
Range:	100 miles / 160km
Recharge Time:	16 hours (or fast charge to 80% in 15 minutes)
Economy:	7km/kWh
Availability:	First North American deliveries in late 2010 with main rollout in 2011. Europe in 2011 and 2012.
Comments:	Not available at time of writing but promises to be the first family sized car to be available as an electric only model.

Peapod

The Peapod is manufactured by Chrysler's GEM division. It is a simple four door, four seat electric NEV for city use.

Originally planned for sale just through GEM dealers, Chrysler has decided to create Peapod as its own brand and sell it through other Chrysler dealers as well.

The Peapod not only feature startling looks, it also has a number of state of the art features, including integration into an iPhone in order to access and drive the car and to provide remote information about the car when you're not around.

The top speed of the car is limited to 25mph in the United States (35mph in some states). There is a lot of excitement about a potential European version of this car with improved performance.

Peapod

Body Styles:	4 door, 4 seat city runabout
Top Speed:	25mph / 40km/h (electronically limited)
Range:	30 miles / 45km
Recharge Time:	6 hours
Economy:	10km/kWh
Availability:	United States – mid 2010, Europe – not known

Peugeot

Peugeot built an electric version of their popular Peugeot 106 from 1995 to 2003. Sold across Europe, the car sold in small numbers through a limited dealer network. There is a small but loyal band of owners and a few specialists who can provide technical services.

Peugeot have recently announced plans to sell a rebranded version of the Mitsubishi i-MiEV in Europe, with sales starting at the beginning of 2011.

106 Electrique

Body Styles:	3 door/5 door hatchback
Top Speed:	60mph / 98km/h
Range:	55 miles
Recharge Time:	8 hours
Economy:	Not Known
Availability:	Second hand only

Phoenix

Phoenix Motorcars are a start-up company converting a range of four wheel drive vehicles manufactured in South Korea by a company called Ssangyong.

Production has been delayed a number of times, not least because Ssangyong have recently undergone a change in ownership and a restructure but production now looks likely to commence during 2010.

SUT

Body Styles:	4 door truck	
Top Speed:	95mph / 152km/h	
Range:	100 miles / 160km	
Recharge Time:	6 hours	
Economy:	Not Known	
Availability:	United States – expected during 2010	

SUV

Body Styles:	5 door SUV	
Top Speed:	95mph / 152km/h	
Range:	100 miles / 160km	
Recharge Time:	6 hours	
Economy:	Not Known	
Availability:	United States – expected during 2010	

Renault

Renault built a small number of electric cars back in the 1990s, predominantly for the French market. Their Clio Electro was a compact, three door hatchback that sold in small numbers. They also produced a small electric van that was used by the French Postal Service.

Most of these early cars are still on the road and make a good choice if you are working to a tight budget and cannot afford a new electric car.

Renault is making big claims about their new electric cars with two new electric cars and one electric van being put on sale at the end of 2010. The largest of these cars, the Fluence Z.E. is a full sized family sedan. European customers will be able to order a Renault electric car from September, 2010 with first deliveries expected to reach customers in the summer of 2011.

Along with partner Better Place, Renault is pioneering a unique battery swap-out system. This allows customers to drive to a

'Quickdrop' centre and swap batteries in around 3-5 minutes. This allows their electric cars to be used on longer distance journeys.

Renault have not yet announced prices for their new cars. However, they have stated the cars will sell for similar amount to a diesel powered equivalent. Batteries will be leased separately.

Clio Electro

Body Styles:	3 door hatchback
Top Speed:	50mph / 80km/h
Range:	50 miles / 80km
Recharge Time:	8 hours
Economy:	Not Known
Availability:	Used only – mainly in France, a few privately exported to other European countries.
Comments:	Built in small numbers between 1995 and 1997.

Twizy Z.E.

Body Styles:	2 seat city car
Top Speed:	46mph / 74km/h
Range:	60 miles / 98km
Recharge Time:	Not Known
Economy:	Not Known
Availability:	Orders taken late 2010. First deliveries in 2011.

Fluence Z.E.

Body Styles:	4 door sedan
Top Speed:	80mph / 128km/h
Range:	100 miles / 160km
Recharge Time:	Not Known
Economy:	Not Known
Availability:	Europe: Orders taken late 2010. First deliveries in mid 2011.

REVA

You may never have heard of them but the REVA Electric Car Company is currently the biggest manufacturer of road going electric cars in the world.

Manufacturing electric cars since 2001, REVA vehicles are sold in Asia, Europe and South America with North American sales and production planned for the near future.

Previous models have all been quadricycles but the new REVA NXR which goes on sale during 2010 is technically classed as a car.

In London, the REVA City has been sold as the G-Wiz. The new REVA NXR is a significantly better car and can compare with combustion engine cars from mainstream manufacturers.

REVA City / G-Wiz

Body Styles:	3 door hatchback
Top Speed:	40mph / 65km/h
Range:	35-40 miles / 55-65km
Recharge Time:	8 hours full charge 80% charge in 2½ hours
Economy:	10km/kWh
Availability:	Used only – mainly in the UK and India.
Comments:	Can seat two adults and two small children. Known as the G-Wiz in the UK and REVA everywhere else. The electric quadricycle that took London by storm.

REVA i / G-Wiz i

Body Styles:	3 door hatchback
Top Speed:	50mph / 80km/h
Range:	43-48 miles / 70-76km
Recharge Time:	8 hours full charge 80% charge in 2½ hours
Economy:	10km/kWh
Availability:	New and used across Europe, central Asia and South America.
Comments:	An updated quadricycle with significantly improved crash protection, handling, ride, braking and performance.

REVA L-ion / G-Wiz L-ion

Body Styles:	3 door hatchback
Top Speed:	50mph / 80km/h
Range:	75 miles / 120km
Recharge Time:	6 hours full charge 80% charge in 45 minutes from fast charging station
Economy:	11km/kWh
Availability:	Available new across Europe, central Asia and South America.
Comments:	A REVA *i* with various improvements, lithium-ion batteries for better performance and a longer range.

REVA NXR

Body Styles:	3 door hatchback
Top Speed:	65mph / 104km/h
Range:	100 miles / 160km/h
Recharge Time:	8 hours
Economy:	Not Known
Availability:	Scheduled for production, first cars will be sold in India, with European sales commencing later in 2010. US likely in 2011.
Comments:	Two versions of the NXR are available – the NXR City is a lower performance version with a range of 50 miles (80km) and the InterCity has lithium-ion batteries with twice the range and significantly better performance.

Mercedes-Smart

Smart have been building two seat city cars for many years. These cars have always *looked* like they ought to be electric powered and originally back in the early 1990s when the cars were conceived, an electric powered prototype was built.

Electric Smart conversions have been available from various specialists since the end of 2005. The specifications for these vehicles vary depending on which company has carried out the conversion.

In 2007, Smart produced 100 prototype electric cars which were leased out to businesses and government agencies in the United Kingdom. These vehicles are likely to be withdrawn in 2010 as a new and improved version of the car is becoming available.

The official Smart electric drive (Smart ED) will only be available in volume production in 2012. Prior to volume production, a limited number of cars are now available and are being leased to customers in the United Kingdom.

Smart ED

Body Styles:	3 door hatchback
Top Speed:	62mph / 100km/h
Range:	84 miles / 134km
Recharge Time:	8 hours full charge
Economy:	Not Known
Availability:	Limited number on lease in the United Kingdom. Smart conversions available from a number of different sources.

Start Lab

Start Lab are an Italian manufacturer building small, two seat electric quadricycles. These have been available for a number of years and they are sold in the United States as the Kurrent.

A small number of Start Lab vehicles were sold in the United Kingdom in 2007, fitted with lithium batteries.

Street

Body Styles:	2 door coupé
Top Speed:	30mph / 45km/h
Range:	30 miles / 45km
Recharge Time:	12 hours full charge
Economy:	10km/kWh
Availability:	Available new across Europe and the United States

Allroad

Body Styles:	2 door coupé
Top Speed:	30mph / 45km/h
Range:	30 miles / 45km
Recharge Time:	12 hours full charge
Economy:	10km/kWh
Availability:	Available new across Europe and the United States

Stevens

Stevens is a small UK based company with the ambition of building a range of electric vehicles in regional factories around the world. Their first car is the spacious, yet compact ZeCar. An electric sports car waits in the wings...

ZeCar

Body Styles:	5 door hatchback
Top Speed:	56mph / 90km/h
Range:	Up to 100 miles / 160km
Recharge Time:	4 hours full charge
Economy:	Unknown
Availability:	United Kingdom

SunMotor

The SunMotor DX Coupe is an electric car with a large solar panel in its roof, creating a genuinely solar powered electric car.

Currently being sold as an NEV, SunMotor is developing a full car version to be launched in early 2011. With a range of up to 160 miles (256km) the DX Coupe's solar roof is large enough to generate up to 15 miles (25km) of charge purely through sun power, depending on the intensity of the sunlight available.

For more information on solar cars and charging electric cars with solar power, see our chapter on solar power starting on page 177.

DX Coupe

Body Styles:	3 door, 2 seat coupe
Top Speed:	25mph / 40km/h
Range:	160 miles / 256km
Recharge Time:	8 hours
Economy:	Not Known
Availability:	United States

Tata

You'll be forgiven for not knowing who Tata is. However, you'll probably know some of the brands. Jaguar, Land Rover, Corus Steel and Tetley Tea are all owned by the Tata Group. They also produce cars, SUVs, vans and trucks that sell mainly in Asia and Africa.

The Tata Indica Vista EV is now available on trial in the United Kingdom, with a small number of vehicles being available for lease. Full production and greater availability for the car is not expected before 2012.

Indica Vista EV

Body Styles:	5 door hatchback
Top Speed:	65mph / 105km/h
Range:	100 miles / 160km
Recharge Time:	12 hours
Economy:	Not Known
Availability:	Strictly limited numbers on lease in the UK. Mainstream production expected in 2012.

Tazzari

Tazzari are a brand new electric car manufacturer based in Italy. Their new car, the Zero, is a two seat 'city sports coupé' with fun handling and strong performance.

Drivers can choose between different driving modes: Economy, Standard, Rain and Race, allowing drivers to choose the right mix of handling, performance and economy at any time.

Zero

Body Styles:	2 door sports
Top Speed:	56mph / 90km/h
Range:	87 miles / 140km/h
Recharge Time:	6-8 hours
Economy:	Not Known
Availability:	Europe and North America.

Tesla

Proof that electric cars don't have to be slow or boring, the Tesla Roadster is the electric car answer to a Porsche or Ferrari.

Available both in North America and in Europe, although there is a long waiting list, the Tesla Roadster provides exceptional performance and impressive economy figures.

The Tesla Roadster out accelerates most Porsche's and Ferrari's and has a range of around 220 miles (although at least one owner has managed to achieve a range of over 300 miles with careful driving). More recently, a Sport version has been announced with even faster performance and custom-tuned suspension for even better handling.

Tesla is one of the fastest growing electric car manufacturers. They manufactured and sold around 1,000 cars in 2009.

Body Styles:	2 door sports
Top Speed:	135mph / 215km/h
Range:	220 miles / 350km
Recharge Time:	3½ hours full charge (with dedicated fast charger)
Economy:	6km/kWh
Availability:	Europe and United States

TH!NK

TH!NK have been designing electric cars since 1991. Purchased by Ford in 1999, the company have manufactured small city cars and electrically assisted bicycles.

Just over 1,000 Think City electric cars were sold worldwide, along with an unknown number of Think Neighbors. Early reliability problems lead Ford to withdraw the Think City from sale and they sold the business in early 2003.

Since then, TH!NK has continued as an independent manufacturer, developing a new city car which has now gone on sale. Production has recently moved from Norway to a Sweden.

City Mk 1

Body Styles: 3 door, 2 seat hatchback

Top Speed: 56mph / 90km/h

Range: 50 miles / 80km

Recharge Time: 8 hours

Economy: Not Known

Availability: Sold between 2000 and early 2003. Most of these cars are still on the roads in Norway and Sweden.

Think Neighbor

Body Styles: 2 seat / 4 seat golf cart

Top Speed: 25mph / 40km/h

Range: 25 miles / 40 km

Recharge Time: 8 hours

Economy: Not Known

Availability: An NEV sold between 1999 and 2002 in California. Most of these vehicles ended their days on the golf course.

City Mk 2

Body Styles: 3 door, 2 seat hatchback

Top Speed: 65mph / 105km/h

Range: 130 miles / 210km

Recharge Time: 8 hours

Economy: Not Known

Availability:	New: across Europe. North American sales will start at some point later in 2010.

Toyota

Toyota does not make electric cars, preferring to concentrate on their hybrid technology. However in 1997, Toyota did launch the RAV4 EV in Japan, Southern California and the Isle of Jersey in the UK. This was an electric version of their popular RAV4 SUV.

The car sold until 2003. Most RAV4s were leased to customers, although a number of customers bought their vehicles outright.

Toyota RAV4 EV

Body Styles:	5 seat SUV
Top Speed:	78mph / 125km/h
Range:	120 miles / 192km
Recharge Time:	5 hours
Economy:	Not Known
Availability:	Only 328 ever built, so few and far between. Cars were sold in California and the English island of Jersey.

Twike

One of the more eccentric electric vehicles available today, the Twike is half way between a bicycle and a car.

Twike sell a version of their vehicle as a hybrid which comes complete with bicycle pedals. 'Hybrid' to Twike means combining human power and electric! The Twike is driven using a joystick.

Although strictly for enthusiasts, over 900 Twikes have been sold worldwide.

Body Styles:	2 seat wedge
Top Speed:	53mph / 95km/h
Range:	125 miles / 200km
Recharge Time:	8 hours
Economy:	Not Known
Availability:	Europe

Venturi

Owned by a former Grand Prix driver, Venturi have been building a tiny number of their Fetish electric sports cars since 2005. For 2010, the Fetish is being joined by the Eclectic – a solar powered three seat vehicle. The company has also been showing a solar powered two seat sports car that may go into production in 2011.

Fetish

Body Styles:	2 door sports car
Top Speed:	105mph / 170km/h
Range:	200 miles / 320km
Recharge Time:	3 hours
Economy:	Not Known
Availability:	Europe
Comments:	Exclusivity is guaranteed as only 25 of these cars will ever be made.

Eclectic

Body Styles:	3 seat buggy
Top Speed:	30mph / 45km/h
Range:	33 miles / 50km
Recharge Time:	5 hours
Economy:	Not Known
Availability:	Europe
Comments:	In direct sunshine, range can be increased by up to 2km per day through the built in solar panel.

Wheego

Wheego distribute a small 2 door coupe across the United States. Currently classed as an NEV, a car version will be on sale in the United States during the summer. Wheego are offering a 50% discount scheme for people buying the NEV version now if they upgrade to the Whip LiFe during 2010 or 2011.

Whip NEV

Body Styles:	2 door coupe
Top Speed:	35mph / 55km/h
Range:	40 miles / 65km
Recharge Time:	10 hours
Economy:	10km/kWh
Availability:	Across United States

Whip LiFe

Body Styles:	2 door coupe
Top Speed:	65mph / 104km/h
Range:	100 miles / 160km
Recharge Time:	Unknown
Economy:	Unknown
Availability:	Across United States
Comments:	A faster, more powerful Whip with all the performance and safety features you would expect from a production car.

ZAP!

ZAP have been successfully selling the Xebra electric three wheel car in the United States since 2006. They have a network of dealers across the country. Cars are available both new and second hand.

Xebra

Body Styles:	5 door hatchback
Top Speed:	40mph / 65km/h
Range:	25 miles / 40km
Recharge Time:	6 hours
Economy:	9km/kWh
Availability:	United States
Comments:	A very small number of these cars have been seen in the United Kingdom and Ireland. European sales are planned for 2010.

ELECTRIC CAR CONVERSIONS

Until recently, if you wanted an electric car, almost the only way you could have one was to convert your own car to electric power, or pay a specialist conversion company to do it for you.

A small number of specialists have offered electric vehicle conversions for years. Some of these are based on a particular make and model of car; others offer a more bespoke service.

Groups like the Battery Vehicle Society (BVS) in the United Kingdom and the Electric Vehicle Association (EVA) in North America cater for enthusiasts who are interested in the engineering aspects of electric vehicles. The BVS run training courses and competitions, have a regular club magazine and arrange regional meetings for electric vehicle enthusiasts. Its members have built thousands of electric vehicles over the years, including the world first road legal solar powered car in 1978.

There are also some excellent books and web sites available. Visit OwningElectricCar.com to see an up-to-date list of web sites.

Most people who choose to carry out a car conversion, or pay for their car to be converted, do so because they cannot find a production electric car that will accomplish what they want.

Many of these conversions are very good. Most conversions use the tried and tested formula of lead acid batteries, DC motor and off-the-shelf motor controller and result in a car with reasonable performance and range.

Some of the cars retain the original gearbox (often without the clutch), others retain the gearbox in order to get the correct gearing for the motor but lock the gearbox in a single gear and remove the gear lever.

The formula is fairly standard and the cars are usually very reliable, serving their owners well for many years.

Not all cars are ideally suited to be converted into an electric car. Big, heavy cars with poor aerodynamics can be converted but the additional cost is significant and the results often perform poorly. As a consequence, most electric conversions are of smaller, lightweight cars which can use smaller motors and battery packs to achieve better results.

Converting a car to electric power is not cheap. A budget conversion on a very small car with a top speed of 35-40mph and a range of 20 miles is likely to cost in the region of £2,000 in the UK (around $3,000 in the United States) for a competent enthusiast to carry out themselves. A professional conversion for a car with highway capable speeds and a range of 100 miles is likely to cost at least £10,000 in the UK or $15,000 in the United States.

You can bring this price down if you're able to get hold of parts for free second hand. Some people have converted their cars using parts from fork-lift trucks and using second hand batteries. If you go this route, you're trading money for time, so expect it to take a lot of time and a lot of effort to complete the project. The result can be a perfectly adequate 'medium speed' electric car. You'll also have the personal satisfaction of knowing that it is all your own handiwork.

Some electric car enthusiasts use kit-cars as a basis for an electric car. Most kit-cars are light weight vehicles and are a good base for building an electric car. Some enthusiasts cover their electric cars in solar panels to create an entirely self-powering car.

Some cars, such as the VW Beetle, have become quite popular as a donor vehicle for converting to electric power. As a consequence, you can buy conversion kits for them. This not only makes the whole job easier, you also benefit from getting a tried and tested product that you know is going to work.

If you are planning to convert a car yourself, you need to have good mechanical skills and a reasonable understanding of electrics in general and vehicle electrics in particular. You will have to fabricate a motor mount and an adaptor plate to connect the motor to the gearbox. If you do not have the skills to fabricate parts yourself, a local machine shop will be able to do this for you.

I would be extremely wary about using lithium-ion batteries on a DIY conversion. Lithium-ion batteries are a temperamental technology and many competent and experienced electric car converters have suffered from complete battery failure, or worse, battery fires that have destroyed the entire vehicle. If you are planning to convert a vehicle yourself, it is strongly advised that you keep the technology as straightforward as possible and use tried-and-tested lead acid battery technology.

As more production electric cars become available, electric car conversions are likely to become a thing of the past as people will be able to buy better and more practical electric cars from mainstream manufacturers.

The exceptions will be a few die-hard individuals working from their garages in the dead of night, powered purely by caffeine, battery fumes and the desire to build something special and unique.

The world would be a poorer place without them.

Chapter Summary

- Converting a car to electric power is for enthusiasts only.

- Don't do it expecting to save lots of money on running costs – the conversion costs are not cheap unless you have a lot of time and access to free, or very low cost, second hand components.

- If you want to go ahead and convert a car yourself, there are various clubs, web sites and societies to help.

- Professional conversions are available. There are a number of companies who carry out electric car conversions.

- Many of these conversions are very good quality and the resulting vehicles are usually very reliable.

- Electric car conversions are likely to be consigned to history as more and more production electric cars become available.

Recharging on the go

One company is looking to the future with intelligent cars and wireless electricity to ensure electric cars always have enough range to do any journey at all and never have to be plugged in to recharge.

Design and engineering company ARUP are at the forefront of electric vehicle infrastructure design, working closely with governments around the world to build the infrastructure for an electric car future.

They are developing an Induction Power Transfer (IPT) system that charges electric cars wirelessly using charging points built into the road or fitted in electric car owner's garages and driveways. The system has no moving parts and can work effectively across a large gap of up to 25cm (10").

The system works using two pads – one built into the road surface sending electricity to the car; and one on the car, receiving the energy and charging the batteries.

The first benefit of the system is that electric car owners don't have to remember to plug their cars. Instead the car starts charging as soon as it is parked.

"IPT charging is intelligent," explains Dick Stimpson, Principal Engineer for Future Transportation. "An intelligent charging system works out how you use the car and charges accordingly. You never have to worry about whether you have enough charge in your car. The car can charge up whenever it is parked and depending on your driving patterns it can choose whether to fast charge or slow charge your car, or to wait until the cost of electricity is low before charging". In case of last minute changes of travel plans, external intervention can be achieved through a mobile phone telephone call to modify the rate of charge to ensure that the car is ready for use when it is needed.

By working out the daily and weekly patterns of car usage, the system has the potential to remove range anxiety forever. With IPT charging installed in car parks and in owner's homes, the electric car itself can make sure it always has enough charge for whatever driving the owner wants to do.

The system works for councils as well. "Councils are being told they have to put in charging points," explains Stimpson. "That currently means a charging post.

This is an issue: they increase street clutter, look untidy and are an ongoing maintenance concern for councils."

"Our system has no moving parts, is installed into the road surface and is cheaper than a charging post."

A static IPT trial is currently under development for electric cars in the UK and an electric bus trial is planned with IPT charging being built into bus stops. When the bus is at a stop, the batteries are recharged. As the bus pulls away from the bus stop, the bus is still receiving power from the system and not the batteries.

The bus is charging even when it is on the move coming to the bus stop and when pulling away. "Electric buses currently don't have the range to be used in our towns and cities", explains Stimpson. "Using IPT charging at bus stops, electric buses can get boost charges to keep them going all day."

Long term, the vision for the IPT system is dynamic charging. Dynamic charging utilizes IPT to charge electric vehicles on the move. Stimpson believes that in the future, dynamic charging will built into major roads, enabling electric cars to recharging as they travel.

Stimpson describes it as a twenty year vision. Building and renovating motorways and freeways is hugely expensive. The incremental cost for building in dynamic charging is negligible. The system would not have to be continuous; it could be installed in strips every few miles. The cars would switch between being powered by batteries and being powered by the dynamic charging system built into the road.

It is not surprising that Stimpson believes that dynamic charging will become the standard way to charge electric cars.

Static IPT charging systems are being installed in the very near future. Dynamic charging is a little way off but its development is exciting. Future electric car owners may never need to worry about range ever again.

BUYING A USED ELECTRIC CAR

For the first time in around 80 years, it is possible in many parts of the world to buy a used electric car.

Over the past twenty years, Ford, Toyota, Honda, General Motors, Fiat, Citroen, Peugeot, Volkswagen and Renault have all built electric cars that have been made available to the public.

Many of the vehicles from the mainstream manufacturers were only available to lease and many were scrapped once the original lease expired. Others, however, have passed into private ownership and occasionally become available on the used car market.

In addition to this, manufacturers like REVA, Think, Aixam, Piaggio, GEM, ZENN, Dynasty and ZAP have been building and selling electric cars in reasonable numbers for a number of years.

Finally, there are a number of cars that have been converted into electric cars and these occasionally appear on the market.

So if you want to buy an electric car but cannot afford to buy a new one, all is not lost, there are still some options available to you.

Do your research

If you find an electric car for sale that you are interested in, it is worth finding out as much information about that particular make and model of car as possible.

Thankfully, the internet is an excellent resource for this sort of research and a lot of owners have posted reviews on their electric cars on various websites.

You will also find a number of web forums dedicated to electric cars. Ask questions; find out the good points and the bad points about the car you are interested in.

Find out if there are any owners of that particular car who live close to where you do and ask if you can visit them and have a ride in their car. Many owners are delighted to be asked and are more than willing to help.

It is also worth talking to the specialist electric car companies who will be able to help you find out more.

A few questions that are worth asking:

- What is the performance like?
- How well does the car cope with driving uphill?
- What range will the car do with good batteries?
- What range will the car do in winter? (most electric cars will have a reduced range in extreme cold)
- How easy is it to get parts for the car and how expensive are they?
- How easy is it to get the car serviced?
- How regularly do the batteries need replacing?
- What is the cost for battery replacement?
- Are there many specialist companies available who can service the cars?
- Are there any common faults with the car and how expensive are these faults to remedy?

If at all possible, go and visit someone who already owns the make and model of electric car that you are considering buying.

Join an owners club

There are quite a few electric car clubs around the world. Some cater in a particular make or model, others cover all electric cars. Some are local, regional clubs; others cover a whole country or are worldwide.

Electric Auto Association in North America and the Battery Vehicle Society in the United Kingdom are the best known car clubs around. There are also manufacturer specific car clubs for

REVA (the REVA Electric Car Club), Tesla, Nissan and Mitsubishi.

Some of these car clubs charge a membership, others are free. If they are free, it may well be worth joining some of these clubs even if they cover models you are not interested in, simply in order to find out more about owners' experiences of driving electric cars in general.

Where to find used electric cars for sale

There are a number of electric car specialists around that supply used electric cars. Some of these sell a specific make and model of electric car; others provide a larger range of vehicles.

A directory of electric car specialists can be found on our website – www.OwningElectricCar.com.

There are a number of electric car clubs and online electric car forums where electric cars are often advertised for sale. Again, you can find a directory of electric car clubs and online forums at www.OwningElectricCar.com.

Finally, used electric cars are regularly advertised on eBay.

What to look for when buying a used electric car

It is important to make sure you inspect an electric car before you buy it and not purchase it unseen.

Most used electric cars have typically been bought as second vehicles. As a result, they are often available with very low odometer readings. 10,000–20,000 miles (16,000–32,000km) for five to ten year old cars is not uncommon.

Mechanically there are a number of areas that you need to check when buying an electric car and so it is important to make sure you ask the seller the right questions.

Conversion or factory made?

First, you will need to find out if the car is a conversion or whether it was built as an electric car by the manufacturer. If it was a conversion, was it a professional conversion by a company with a track record of converting cars to electric power or was it converted at home.

If the car was converted by the owner, check the quality of the work carried out. Is everything neat? Are the cables tidy? Is everything screwed together properly? Are the batteries mounted properly? If the work looks sloppy, there may be further problems with the vehicle that you can't see.

It is fairly unusual for home converted electric cars to be sold on, so if the car is a home conversion ask the owner why they are selling it.

Brakes

The mechanical brakes tend to be underused on an electric car. This is because of regenerative braking. As a consequence, it is not unusual for a ten year old electric car to be still on its original brake pads and shoes.

This underuse can lead to sticking brakes, where one or more of the wheel brakes does not release when the brake pedal is lifted.

This issue affects the performance and range of the car, as well as wearing out the brakes prematurely.

Ask the owner if they have had any problems with sticking brakes. Also make sure you test the brakes properly when test driving an electric car.

Batteries

The biggest single issue with used electric cars is the condition of the batteries.

Most used electric cars will have either lead acid or nickel metal hydride battery packs. Lithium-ion battery packs are relatively new to electric cars and have not made it to the used electric car market yet.

The reason batteries can be such an issue is the down to the replacement cost of batteries. Lead acid batteries will require replacement every three to five years. Nickel metal hydride batteries may last considerably longer, but the cost is significantly higher when they do require replacement.

Find out when the batteries were last checked and/or replaced and ask if there are any known battery problems with the vehicle.

Some batteries require topping up with distilled water on a regular basis. It is important to ensure the watering has been carried out according to the manufacturer's instructions as not watering the batteries will cause premature battery failure.

Unfortunately, it is not always possible to identify battery issues purely from a test drive, although there are some tests that you can do that will help you identify any potential issues. These are described in *the test drive* section.

Motor

There are various different types of electric motor. From a maintenance point of view, they fall into two categories: brushed and brushless motors.

If the electric car you are looking at has a brushed motor, it is important to ensure the motor brushes have been regularly checked, cleaned and replaced where necessary. Brushes are the lifeline of a brushed motor and wear with use. If they are not regularly checked and cleaned, the motor will perform poorly and eventually break.

Replacement motor brushes for brushed motors are cheap and the brushes should be checked every six months, or as per the manufacturer's recommendations, whichever is the sooner.

Heating

Check that the heating works. Unlike conventional cars where the heating uses the wasted heat from the engine compartment, an electric car has to have a separate heating system.

Some of these systems work better than others and many home conversions in particular do suffer from poor heating. Many electric cars use fuel heaters (they run on diesel) which produce a lot of heat very quickly. Although these are very effective, they can be expensive and difficult to repair if they break.

Getting expert advice

If you are not buying from a local electric vehicle specialist, you may prefer an expert to check the car on your behalf.

Thankfully, that is not as daunting as you may think. Although electric cars may be few and far between on our roads, there are a huge number of electric vehicles in use around the world. Airport vehicles, golf carts and warehouse vehicles such as fork lift trucks are in use everywhere and there are specialist companies providing electric vehicle maintenance in every major town and city.

Most electric vehicle service engineers are mobile and carry out electric vehicle servicing at a customer's premises.

There are a number of companies offering these services, so you should not find it difficult to find someone who will be able to carry out an assessment on an electric car.

If you wish to do this, make sure the seller is happy for an engineer to carry out a full assessment on the vehicle. Sometimes batteries are mounted in difficult to access areas which may involve removing seats or interior trim in order to check them properly.

The test drive

When you arrange to inspect an electric car that is for sale, ask for the car to be fully charged before you arrive and ensure that you can carry out a lengthy test drive in order to assess the performance and range of the car.

The main purposes for the test drive are threefold:

- To make sure the car suits your needs.
- To ensure there are no obvious mechanical or electrical faults.
- To ensure the batteries are working well.

Before you take the car out on a test drive, ask the seller what range the vehicle should do and ask him to describe the sort of driving he would be doing in order to achieve that range – i.e. across town, stop start or on open roads. Find out the sort of speeds he would be doing when achieving that range.

You can use this information as a benchmark for your own test drive.

Choose a route that will match the sort of driving that you would normally be doing on a regular basis but at the same time make sure there is a mix of roads so you can see how well the car performs in different circumstances.

When you start driving, spend a few minutes driving the car and making sure you are comfortable with it. The lack of engine noise does take some getting used to, as does the slightly different power delivery from the electric motor and the regenerative braking.

Once you have had time to get used to the characteristics of the car, get a feel for the performance of the car.

You will usually find that acceleration from a standing start is good and around town the car should feel reasonably nippy.

Some small electric cars with lower power brushed motors may not be particularly quick up hills. Drive up a couple of hills and make sure you are happy with the performance.

If possible, it is a good idea to find a flat, clear road to see how well the car performs at speed. You will usually find low end acceleration is good but higher end acceleration is not so responsive. It is worth seeing if the car can maintain the speed claimed by the seller.

Weak batteries rarely show themselves when the batteries are charged up, they only start causing problems as the charge drops.

As the battery charge drops, it is worth doing these same tests again. On this second series of tests, if the car appears to be sluggish at low speeds, or struggles on hills or cannot maintain its top speed on a flat road, it suggests that the batteries may be getting tired and may require replacement.

If you can hear a hissing sound or the smell of rotten eggs coming from the battery compartment during your test, stop the car. The batteries are failing. Stop the car immediately and wait for the batteries to cool down.

To make sure you don't run out of charge, it is worth ensuring that you remain close to the seller's location when carrying out these tests as the batteries are running down. If there are battery problems they can fail quite suddenly, you don't want to end up stranded a long way from base if that happens!

Incidentally, if you do suffer from a sudden battery failure, the answer is to stop the car, leave the batteries to recover for around 20 minutes and then drive slowly back to base.

If the batteries are failing, you will need to factor in the cost of a new set of batteries into the cost of purchasing the vehicle.

Servicing your used electric car

If you are buying a used electric car, you may not have the same servicing options available to you as you do with a new car.

Start by talking to the manufacturer or importer of the car who will have servicing facilities in place. Check they cover your area.

Alternatively, if you are lucky enough to live close to an electric car specialist, it is a good idea to let them service your car for you.

If you are buying a used electric car from a major company like Ford, Citroen, Peugeot or Toyota, you should be able to get the car serviced by your local dealer. However, that is not always the case. Some of the limited volume electric cars built by mainstream manufacturers in the 1990s are no longer supported by the dealer network. Talk to your local dealer and find out.

If none of that works, speak to a company who service and maintain fork lift trucks. Many of them will be happy to maintain the electrical side of your car for you and the brakes, steering and suspension can be maintained by any local garage.

Finally, you can choose to service and maintain your car yourself. If you decide to go this route, it is worth investigating to see if there is an owners club for your particular model, or join a group such as the Battery Vehicle Society or the Electric Auto Association in order to talk to other owners who have done this.

Chapter Summary

- Do your research into the models you are interested in.
- Find other owners on the internet and ask lots of questions.

- You can find used cars for sale through EV specialists, electric car clubs, online electric car forums and on eBay.

- You need to check brakes, motor, batteries and heating.

- Professional help is available from mobile electric vehicle specialists – although they are usually more used to maintaining fork lift trucks!

- A long test drive, in order to test the batteries, is a must.

- There are various options available for getting your used electric car serviced. Find out what they are before you buy your car.

ELECTRIC CARS AND THE ENVIRONMENT

Few subjects are more emotive than the environment and when it comes to electric cars everybody seems to have an opinion. Claims and counter claims are made and after a while it becomes difficult to identify folklore from fact.

I'm not going to use this book to jump into the climate change debate. Instead, I will do my best to explain the environmental impacts of electric cars and how they compare with conventional combustion engine cars.

Before we begin

I have gone into this section in a fair amount of detail. This is the only way to explain the 'big picture' about the environmental impact of transport, both electric and otherwise.

Some people may not want this level of information. So I have tried to keep it interesting and not get embroiled in the mathematics.

Others need to understand the environmental case for and against electric cars in great detail and won't be satisfied until they have got it. I hope I have gone into enough detail to satisfy everyone. If I have missed something, I have included references to all the studies and reports I refer to.

How to create a comparison between electric cars and conventional cars

Electric car enthusiasts are always keen to point out the fact that their cars do not produce any pollution where they are being used. Detractors point to the coal-fired power station generating the electricity in the first place.

Both groups are making a valid point but taken in isolation both groups are not looking at the whole picture. Without looking at the bigger picture, no fair assessment of the relative merits and disadvantages of different technologies and vehicle types can be made.

The European Commission have defined a standard way for measuring the emissions from cars, based on their carbon dioxide emissions from the exhaust of the car. This is measured in grams of carbon dioxide per km travelled (CO_2 g/km).

This is known as a 'tank to wheel' measurement. A measurement of emissions from the point the fuel has been pumped into the fuel tank to the point where the energy is used.

Of course, electric cars benefit significantly from this measurement because by themselves they do not pollute at all.

However, in the same way that a 'tank to wheel' measurement does not measure the true carbon footprint of using an electric car, neither does it measure the true carbon footprint of using a conventional combustion engine car. The carbon footprint for extracting, refining and transporting the oil in the first place also needs to be taken into account.

This measurement is called a 'well to wheel' measurement and in order to be able to make a true comparison between electric cars and combustion engine cars, we need to be able to identify this well to wheel calculation for both oil and electricity.

There are several measurements that need to be considered when comparing the environmental impact of a combustion engine car with an electric car:

- Air pollution.
- How the energy (both fuel for combustion engines and electricity) is produced and transported.
- Fuel economy
- The environmental impact of batteries
- Vehicle manufacturing and recycling

I have structured this chapter to discuss these measurements separately. At the end of the chapter I then pull the separate threads together to provide a suitable comparison between combustion engine cars and electric cars.

104

An acknowledgement to Motor Manufacturers

There is a tendency for environmental groups to cast the big motor manufacturers, along with 'Big Oil' as the environmental demons of the known world.

You don't need to look far on the internet to start finding conspiracies about motor manufacturers and big oil producers working in collusion; or see pictures of big, old factories pumping out high levels of emissions while all the time building bigger and more powerful SUVs.

Yet over the past twenty years, car manufacturers have done more to improve the environmental performance of their products than any other industry.

Cars are bigger and heavier than twenty years ago. This has been driven by customer demand for larger cars and higher levels of comfort and safety. Despite this, fuel economy, fuel emissions and engine efficiency has all improved.

More recycled materials are being used to build new cars, making a significant reduction in raw material usage. In addition, around 95% of a new car can now be recycled at the end of its useful life.

Of course, much of this improvement has been down to legislation but manufacturers have also been taking the initiative in making a better quality product that is more environmentally friendly than ever before.

There is still a long way to go and by no means am I saying that motor manufacturers are perfect but it is still a point worth making. Above almost any other industry, the motor industry knows their products have got to be more environmentally efficient. They have been taking the appropriate steps to make sure that happens.

Air Pollution

Whatever your opinions on climate change, there is no doubt that we suffer from over-pollution in our towns and cities.

In Germany, it is estimated that over 65,000 people die prematurely every year as a result of excessive air pollution. Across

Europe air pollution reduces life expectancy by around nine months, while in some European countries the average is closer to 1-2 years[6].

Worldwide, two million people die each year as a result of excessive air pollution[7] and tens of millions of people suffer from pollution related illnesses, such as heart and lung diseases, chest pains and breathing difficulties[8] [9].

Worldwide, air pollution is now seen as a major public health issue and not just an environmental issue.

The current view on Air Pollution from Traffic

Transportation gets a lot of criticism for creating air pollution. There is no doubt that it is one of the major contributing causes of air pollution, but it is by no means the only one. Industry and homes all create air pollution that also needs to be addressed (I discuss air pollution from power stations on page 112).

There are reasons why traffic pollution has been singled out by scientists, politicians and policy makers as the most significant pollution issue and why traffic pollution is particularly harmful:

- Worldwide, industrial and domestic pollutant sources are generally improving over time. Worldwide, traffic pollutions are becoming worse[10].

- Tiny particles within vehicle exhaust, known as particulate matters (PM), are particularly dangerous when breathed in. Particulate matters penetrate deep into the lungs and in some

---

[6]EC study – Thematic Strategy on Air Pollution, COM(2005) 446 final, 21.09.2005

[7]World Health Org: Fact Sheet No. 313 – Air Quality and Health.

[8]Air Pollution-Related Illness: Effects of Particles: Andre Nel, Department of Medicine, University of California. Published by the AAAS

[9]The Merck manual for healthcare professionals: Pulmonary Disorders.

[10]Air Pollution in the UK: 2007. AEA Energy and the Environment, commissioned by DEFRA and the Devolved Administrations, UK.

cases directly into the bloodstream where they have the potential to affect internal organs[11].

- Vehicle exhaust emits both volatile organic compounds (VOCs) and nitrogen oxide (NO_x). When combined with sunlight, this creates a complex chemical reaction, creating ozone. When inhaled in relatively small amounts, even by relatively healthy people, ozone can cause chest pain, coughing, shortness of breath and throat irritation.

- Carbon monoxide emissions from traffic exhaust can enter the bloodstream and reduces oxygen delivery to the body's organs and tissues.

- Toxic Organic Micro Pollutants (TOMPS), produced by the incomplete combustion of fuels comprise of a complex range of chemicals that can be highly toxic or carcinogenic. TOMPS can cause a wide range of effects, from cancer to reduced immunity to the nervous system and can interfere with child development. There is no 'threshold dose'. Even the tiniest amount can cause damage.[12]

- Traffic pollution is the number one cause of particulate matter and carbon monoxide emissions in the world and a major contributor to VOC, nitrogen oxide and TOMP emissions.[13]

- In built up areas, traffic can create very high levels of pollution. This often creates visible smog that does not easily clear. This high level of pollution results in very high human exposure to these emissions.

Diesel Pollution

Emissions from diesel vehicles are particularly nasty. Carbon dioxide emissions are comparatively low, but nitrous and other

---

[11]EUROPA research into air quality at the European Commission MEMO/07/108, 20/03/2007

[12]Air Pollution in the UK: 2007. AEA Energy and the Environment, commissioned by DEFRA and the Devolved Administrations, UK.

[13]University of Strathclyde Energy Systems Research Unit: Environmental Pollution from Road Transport.

particulates in the emissions have been shown to be harmful to human health and are a significant issue with local air quality in many cities.

Diesel exhaust (known as Diesel Particulate Matter – or DPM) has been shown to cause acute short term symptoms such as dizziness, headaches and nausea and breathing difficulties. Long term exposure can lead to chronic health problems such as cardiovascular disease and lung cancer.[14]

In 1998, the California Air Resources Board identified diesel particulate matter as a 'toxic air contaminate' based on its potential to cause cancer, premature death and other health problems. The American Lung Association estimates that DPM causes 4,700 premature deaths annually in nine of America's major cities.

Diesel Particulate Matter is particularly dangerous as many of the particles are very small, making them almost impossible to filter out and very easy for human lungs to absorb.

Four things have been introduced to reduce DPM pollution:

- Fuel companies have introduced Ultra-Low Sulphur Diesel (ULSD). Otherwise known as 'clean' diesel, ultra-low sulphur diesel has approximately 3% of the sulphur found in normal diesel. This reduces the amount of soot found in diesel emissions, with only a very slight impact on peak power and fuel economy.

- Car manufacturers have developed their modern diesel engines, to become significantly more efficient at burning their own emissions, thereby reducing the quantities of DPM being released into the atmosphere and significantly decreasing carbon monoxide emissions.

- Modern diesel engines have complex filtration to filter out the larger particles.

---

[14]University of Strathclyde Energy Systems Research Unit: Environmental Pollution from Road Transport.

California Environmental Protection Agency: Air Resources Board. Diesel Health Effects.

- Many commercial diesel engines now have a urea-injection system to inject urea into the exhaust in order to convert harmful nitrogen oxide gas into ammonia and nitrogen.

  o Ammonia is still a toxic gas that can be fatal if inhaled directly and is an highly reactive environmental pollutant. Yet it is still better than the nitrogen oxide it replaces.

These advances are very welcome and will save thousands of lives around the world. Yet despite the advances, diesel pollution remains an issue. While the advances in diesel development are to be welcomed and encouraged, the fact remains that diesel pollution is still a significant concern.

Compared to an equivalent petrol (gasoline) engine, a modern 'clean' diesel engine is likely to produce 20-30 times more nitrous emissions, as well as particulate matter which the petrol/gasoline engine does not. However, both carbon dioxide and carbon monoxide levels will be lower on the diesel engine than on an equivalent petrol/gasoline engine.

Biodiesel Pollution

Biodiesel is often mixed with diesel. In Europe, diesel purchased from a service station will typically have a 5% biodiesel mix and 15% and 30% mixes (called Biodiesel B15 and Biodiesel B30) are now regularly available in many parts of Europe.

Only product sold as 'Biodiesel B100' is 100% biodiesel. All other biodiesels are a blend of biodiesel and diesel.

Biodiesel and some biodiesel blends are not compatible with all diesel engines. If you are planning to use biodiesel with your car, check with the manufacturer first that your engine will run on it.

Biodiesel can be made from many different sources. The most common is plant oil produced from rapeseed, corn and maize. However, biodiesel production has been blamed increasing food prices and causing starvation in the third world. It is also being blamed for increased deforestation in the Amazon rain forests.

Now, new 'second generation' bio-fuels are being developed that do not use food crops. Instead they use the waste from food crop production to make fuel. Other biodiesel is being made from algae, decaying plants and even landfill waste to create fuel.

Biodiesel has been touted by many as a 'clean' fuel because of its significantly lower carbon dioxide and carbon monoxide emissions and its virtual eradication of sulphur from the exhaust.

For this reason, there is no doubt that biodiesel can vastly improve air quality from traffic pollution.

However, nitrogen oxide emissions in biodiesel are significantly higher than other diesel fuels. Nitrogen Oxide is almost 300 times more powerful as a greenhouse gas than carbon dioxide.

This is one of the many reasons why questions have been raised as to whether biodiesel has any benefit in terms of solving climate change issues. There have been many claims that bio-fuels may actually increase greenhouse gas emissions rather than decrease it[15].

Average Petrol/Gasoline and Diesel Emissions (per litre[16]) from fuel tank to wheel[17]:

	Carbon Dioxide	Carbon Monoxide	Nitrogen Oxide	Sulphur Dioxide
Petrol/ Gasoline	2,315g 5 pounds 1oz	140g 5oz	9.5g 3½oz	Trace[18]
ULS Diesel	2,630g 5 pounds 13oz	237g 8½oz	37g 1¹⁄₃oz	Trace[19]
B100 bio diesel	1,736g 3 pounds 13oz	117g 4oz	40g 1½oz	Nil

[15]Atmospheric Chemistry and Physics: N_2O release from agro-biofuel production negates global warming reduction. Atmos. Chem. Phys. Discuss., 7, 11191-11205, 2007

[16]To convert these figures into emissions per gallon, multiply the figures by 3.79 for a US gallon; or by 4.55 for an Imperial gallon.

[17]Source: US National Vehicle and Fuel Emissions Laboratory / BP Fuels

[18]Sulphur-free petrol, containing less than 10 parts per million, became mandatory in 2009 across the EU. US figures may vary.

[19]Sulphur-free diesel, containing less than 10 parts per million, became mandatory in 2009 across the EU. US figures may vary.

Please note: This table is based on average emissions for cars and light goods vehicles in the United States. The exact amount of carbon monoxide, sulphur dioxide and nitrogen oxide will vary significantly from one engine design to another and will also vary depending on how efficiently the engine is running.

A word about asthma and traffic pollution

Over the past thirty years, there has been a huge rise in the number of asthma sufferers around the world. Many environmental groups claim air pollution is the cause.

The figures on asthma are certainly shocking. In the United States, asthma rates have increased 70% in the past thirty years and are up 160% in children under the age of five. 8.9% of all children in the USA are now diagnosed with asthma.[20]

In the UK, around 9% of all children and 8% of all adults are currently receiving treatment for asthma[21] and similar trends can be seen across the whole of Europe and Canada.

Research into what is causing this large increase of asthma cases is still ongoing, especially in California where new evidence has emerged that may yet link the asthma with traffic pollution.

However, based on a number of studies carried out in Ireland, the UK, Canada, France and the USA, the general consensus in all these countries is that there is currently little evidence that there is a definitive link between the cause of asthma and air pollution.

There are, however, many indicators that suggest that the causes lie elsewhere. Most asthma specialists believe that the cause is most probably in the home where higher levels of insulation and heating over the past thirty years are creating the ideal environment for dust mites, with the asthma being caused by humans breathing in these tiny dust particles.[22] [23]

---

[20]American Academy of Allergy, Asthma and Immunology

[21]Asthma UK

[22]UK Department for Health Report: Asthma and outdoor air pollution, ISBN 011321958x

111

Although air pollution may not be the cause of asthma, many people who already have asthma do report increased asthma attacks as a direct result of traffic pollution: this link between *asthma attacks* and air pollution is well known by asthma specialists.

In a recent study in Wales, 65% of asthma sufferers said they suffered coughing fits and shortness of breath as a result of traffic congestion. Research in the USA has suggested similar figures[24].

When questioned, many asthma sufferers say they cannot walk or shop in congested areas because traffic pollution triggers breathing problems.[25]

Air Pollution from Electricity Power Stations

The amount of air pollution generated from an electricity power station varies. It is based on a number of factors, including:

- What fuel is being used to generate the electricity (coal, coke, oil, gas, biomass and so on).

- The quality of the fuel used (not all coal or oil is created alike).

- The efficiency of the power station.

- The filtration used to clean the emissions before they are released into the atmosphere.

Air pollution from electricity power stations is reducing. Even existing power stations are producing lower emissions than ever before as they switch to lower carbon fuels, install particulate and sulphur filters and become more efficient at generating electricity.

There is still a very long way to go before most countries have 'clean' electricity. Many countries are reliant on coal or gas for the production of most of their electricity. Moving away from these to cleaner energy sources is going to take many years.

Here are average figures for pollution for each kWh of electricity generated by different types of electricity power station:

---

[23]American Journal of Respiratory and Critical Care Medicine (1999; 159:125-29)

[24]American Academy of Allergy, Asthma and Immunology

[25]Asthma UK opinion research, 21st September, 2007.

Power Station Average Emissions (per kWh of electricity generated)[26]:

	Carbon Dioxide	Carbon Monoxide	Nitrogen Oxide	Sulphur Dioxide
Coal	990g 2 pounds 3oz	0.2g < 1/100th oz	2.8g 1/10th oz	2.7g 1/10th oz
Gas	400g 15oz	0.1g < 1/200th oz	0.4g 1/70th oz	Trace
Oil	740g 1 pound 11oz	0.4g 1/70th oz	3.2g 1/9th oz	1.5g 1/20th oz
Nuclear	16g ½ oz	Nil	Nil	Nil
Geo-thermal	122g 4½ oz	Nil	Nil	1.0g 1/28th oz
Hydro-electric	Nil	Nil	Nil	Nil
Wind turbine	Nil	Nil	Nil	Nil
Solar	Nil	Nil	Nil	Nil

Average CO_2 emissions for electricity generation

Every nation has a different mix of power stations to generate their power. The US, Australia and India all have a high dependency on coal, France uses nuclear power, and Norway and Sweden generate most of their electricity using hydro-electric power stations.

The result is there are significant differences in the average emissions for electricity production from country to country.

---

[26] I have various sources for this information – including discussions with representatives from EDF Energy, both in France and in the UK, E-ON and the UK National Grid, plus documented sources from the IEA Energy Technology Perspectives 2008 paper, the Laboratory for Energy and the Environment at the Massachusetts Institute of Technology and the Icelandic Energy Authority.

Emissions from National Energy Mix by Country:[27]

Country	CO_2 emissions per kWh
Austria	221g (8 ounces)
Australia	936g (2 pounds)
Canada	234g (8½ ounces)
Denmark	308g (11 ounces)
France	87g (3 ounces)
Finland	261g (9½ ounces)
Germany	453g (1 pound)
Greece	781g (1 pound 11 ounces)
Iceland	138g (5 ounces)
India	930g (2 pounds)
Ireland	573g (1 pound 4½ ounces)
Italy	455g (1 pound)
Japan	429g (15½ ounces)
Nepal	1g ($^1/_{28}$ ounce)
New Zealand	275g (10 ounces)
Norway	7g (¼ ounce)
Pakistan	380g (14 ounces)
Spain	452g (1 pound)
Sweden	57g (2 ounces)
United Kingdom	537g (1 pound 3 ounces)
United States of America	609g (1 pound 6 ounces)

How our energy is produced

Whether we are using gasoline, petrol, diesel or electricity to fuel our cars, we need to understand how our energy is being produced in order to understand the full 'well to wheel' energy usage of our vehicles.

---

[27] Sources: International Energy Agency Data Services/Carbon Trust.

How gasoline, petrol and diesel are produced

Oil Extraction

Crude oils can be found at varying depths in the earth's crust, either on land or under water. Oil is typically found trapped in sandstone along with natural gas and salt water, often at high pressure.

The texture and chemical makeup of oil varies from oil field to oil field. In some fields, the oil is like tar (so called 'heavy crude'), whereas in others the oil is very thin and light ('light crude'). The chemical makeup varies too and is typically graded by its sulphur content. Low sulphur content oil is called 'sweet' while high sulphur content oil is 'sour'. Some crude oils are black or brown; others are red, green, yellow or orange.

The most valuable oil is 'light, sweet' crude oil as this yields a higher amount of automotive and aerospace fuels once refined.

Oil is released by drilling a well into the side of the formation. Tap the peak of the formation and you will only extract gas, tap too far to the side of the formation and you will only get salt water.

The oil normally pushes itself up out of the well because of the natural pressure found inside the oil seam. It often reaches the surface with quite some force.

As oil comes up out of the well, water is pumped back into the well to replace the oil that has been extracted. This maintains the pressure levels within the well, easing the further extraction of oil.

Most oil fields have multiple wells, extracting both oil and natural gas. The oil and gas is either piped directly to a refinery, or loaded onto ships for onward transportation to a refinery.

Along with oil and gas, sand, salt and water is extracted from the well. As the oil fields get older, more and more sand, salt and water are extracted. In some oil fields, 99% of the extracted liquid is salt water. The oil is extracted from the salt water and sand as part of the extraction process. The more filtering that needs to be done, the higher the cost of extraction, to the point where it becomes uneconomic to continue operating near-exhausted oil fields.

Getting fuel from crude oil

Crude oil cannot simply be pumped into a car engine and used as fuel. Crude oil is a mixture of different components (called fractions). Some fractions are highly combustible, light and runny; some fractions are thick, heavy, inflammable tar-like sludge and other fractions are somewhere in between the two.

As crude oil, these different fractions are all mixed together into one liquid. To make crude oil into a useful material, it first needs to be separated, converted and treated.

This is the work that is carried out at an oil refinery.

An oil refinery transforms crude oil into lots of different products:

- Bitumen (tar) is a heavy, inflammable liquid used for the production of road surfaces and roofing materials.
- Fuel oil is another heavy liquid used in oil fired power stations and large industrial engines.
- Lubricating oils such as grease and used for making oil based polishes.
- Diesel
- Kerosene is used in the production of jet fuel, paraffin and heating oil.
- Petrol / Gasoline.
- Naphtha is used in the production of plastics.
- Petroleum Gas is used for making LPG and bottled gases.

Hot crude oil is pumped into a distillation tower where it continues to be heated. As the different densities of oil heat up, the crude separates into fractions according to weight and boiling point, at which point they can be extracted.

Lighter oils, such as LPG and petrol, evaporates under heat and rises to the top of the tower, kerosene and diesel remain near the middle and heavier liquids, such as lubricating oil and tar remain at the bottom.

These different fractions are then tapped off and are taken off for further treatment.

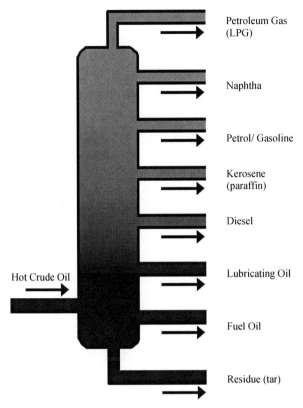

Figure 7 - A diagram of a distillation tower, where crude oil is separated into different categories of oil by heating it.

Only some of the crude oil is suitable for road fuels, with the rest being used for other purposes. However, the demand for petrol and gasoline is so high, oil refineries need to be able to create more road fuel from crude oil than is possible through distillation alone.

In order to do this, some of the low-value heavier oils go through an energy intensive process known as catalytic cracking. Oils are pumped into a reactor and heated to an intense heat and pressure. Using a catalyst, catalytic cracking then converts most of the heavy fractions into lighter fractions such as petrol/gasoline.

Some oil refineries have another energy intensive process called coking. This is used to break down very heavy fractions (tar and lubricating oil) into lighter oils, leaving a residue of coke – a hard, high carbon, coal like substance that is used as an industrial fuel and can be burnt like coal at many coal-fired power stations.

Once petrol, gasoline and diesel have been extracted from the crude oil, they undergo further treatments. These treatments include blending, purifying and adding additives to improve performance. Petrol companies often blend their fuel to suit the weather to ensure the best performance in different conditions.

On average, oil refineries are around 88% efficient at converting crude oil to refined oil[28]. This is an extremely high level of efficiency for any manufactured product.

'Well to Service Station' efficiency for car fuels

According to the United States Department for Energy, the average 'oil well to service station' efficiency for car fuels is 83%[29].

This figure includes transportation of crude oil to the refinery, the refining of the oil and the transportation to the service station.

Based on this calculation, you can divide the average fuel emissions by 0.83 – or multiply by 1.205 – in order to calculate an approximate 'well to wheel' emissions of petrol, gasoline or diesel powered cars:

Average Petrol/Gasoline and Diesel CO_2 Emissions (per litre[30]) from the oil well to wheel[31]:

Fuel	CO_2 emissions per litre
Petrol/Gasoline	2,789g (6 pounds, 3½ ounces)
ULS Diesel	3,168g (7 pounds, 1 ounce)

---

[28]Source: Estimation of Energy Efficiencies of U.S. Petroleum Refineries, Michael Wang. Center for Transportation Research. Argonne National Laboratory. March 2008.

[29]Source: DOE. Electric and Hybrid Vehicle Research, Development and Demonstration Program; Petroleum-Equivalent Fuel Economy Calculation

[30]To convert these figures into emissions per gallon, multiply the figures by 3.79 for a US gallon; or by 4.55 for an Imperial gallon.

[31]Source: Discussions with representatives from BP Global and figures from the US National Vehicle and Fuel Emissions Laboratory.

Where our electricity comes from

As already discussed on page 112, our electricity comes from various sources and each source has a very different carbon footprint.

Managing these sources and ensuring that electricity supply always matches with demand is not a straightforward process. If supply does not match demand, the result is either a brownout or a blackout. A brownout is a voltage loss that causes lights to flicker or dim and causes electronic equipment to reset. A blackout is a complete power failure.

Electricity is delivered from the power stations to homes and businesses through power grids. These grids typically cover an entire country, often with interconnections between countries, which allows exporting and importing of power to cope with different peaks and troughs in different countries at different times.

Some power stations run constantly, while others are adjusted to cope with demand. Nuclear power stations, for example, run at a constant output and as a consequence are often used as a 'base load'. Coal, gas and oil fired power stations can provide greater or lesser power depending on demand and many may spend some of each day generating no power at all.

This means that it is not always obvious where your electricity is generated from. You could live next to a coal fired power station but outside of peak times your actual electricity may actually be generated by a wind turbine half way across the country.

Your power might not even come from your own country. Canada, for example, supplies the United States with electricity and the whole of Europe now has electricity interconnections between different countries.

Theoretically, the longest cost-effective distance for transmitting electricity is 7,000km (4,300 miles)[32]. At present all transmission lines are considerably shorter, but the likely emergence of renewable power super grids spanning entire continents in the next

---

[32]Global Energy Network Institute library paper: Present Limits of Very Long Distance Transmission Systems

few years means it is not inconceivable that in the near future, a person living in Scotland could be using solar electricity produced in the Sahara.

Demand for electricity goes up and down at different times of the day.

A typical day in the UK for electricity demand would look something like this:

- Demand for electricity is very low throughout the night and early morning.

- There is a jump in power demand at around 8 o'clock in the morning.

- The demand then rises gradually throughout the morning, often with a mini-peak at around 10:30.

- Demand gradually rises during the afternoon, jumping up considerably at around 4 o'clock.

- Peak demand starts at around 5 o'clock in the evening and continues until around 7:30pm after which the demand for power gradually decreases, dropping rapidly again after 10 o'clock at night.

In the UK, the majority of the 'base load' (i.e. the minimum amount of power required on the national grid) is provided by gas, hydro-electric and nuclear power stations.

UK 'Peak load' electricity that handles the different levels of demand throughout the day is provided by gas, coal, and oil and pumped storage power stations (a description of each of these is included later in this chapter).

Wind turbines contribute power depending on the amount of energy they are producing at any one time. As we cannot rely on the wind blowing at the right time, it is difficult to factor wind energy into managing peaks and troughs in energy demand.

Coal fired power stations

Coal fired power stations generate the highest emissions of all for generating electricity. Worldwide, approximately 41% of all electricity is generated from coal fired power stations[33], while around 49% of electricity in the United States is generated from coal.

Coal has achieved this position of dominance because of price and flexibility. Coal fired power stations can use cheap coal to generate electricity at a price that is difficult for other fuels to compete with. At the same time, coal fired power stations are reasonably flexible with their power output. When demand increases, they can boost their power generation accordingly and drop back again when demand decreases.

According to the World Coal Institute, if we continue to use coal at our current rate, we will have enough to last us another 130 years.

Like oil, the makeup of coal varies depending on where it is mined from. Coal is an organic rock made up of varying combinations of carbon, hydrogen, oxygen, nitrogen and sulphur.

Coal is 'ranked' based on its chemical and physical properties. Low ranked coals are low in carbon but high in hydrogen and oxygen, while high ranked coals are high in carbon but low in hydrogen and oxygen.

Low ranked coals are less efficient to burn than high ranked coals, creating more ash and soot. As a consequence they cost less to buy. For this reason, most coal fired power stations are designed to use the lowest ranking of coal available.

According to the Union of Concerned Scientists, in an average year a typical coal fired power station emits:

- 3,700,000 ton of carbon dioxide (CO_2)
- 10,000 ton of sulphur dioxide (SO_2)
- 500 ton of particulate matters (PM)
- 10,200 ton of nitrogen oxide (NO_x)
- 720 ton of carbon monoxide (CO)
- 220 ton of volatile organic compounds (VOCs)
- Small amounts of mercury, arsenic, lead, cadmium and uranium.

---

[33]Source: World Coal Institute

In addition to the air pollution, the average coal fired power station creates around 125,000 ton of ash and 193,000 ton of 'sludge'. This waste includes toxic substances such as arsenic, mercury, chromium and cadmium. In the United States, 75% of this waste is disposed of in unmonitored on-site landfills[34].

The largest single source of pollution in Europe is the Drax Power Station in North Yorkshire, United Kingdom. Its generating capacity of almost 4,000 megawatts of electricity is the highest of any power station in Europe. At any one time it is providing around 7% of the United Kingdom's electricity.

In 2008, Drax emitted 23,019,596 ton of carbon dioxide, 24,500 ton of sulphur dioxide, 38,250 ton of nitrogen oxide and 470 ton of particulate matters. 1,461,000 ton of ash was created by the plant, of which 866,000 ton were recycled and sold to the construction industry and 595,000 ton was placed in landfill[35].

In addition, an estimated 249,000 ton of carbon dioxide emissions were generated as a result of transporting coal to the power station.

Although Drax is the largest polluting power station in Europe, it is not the worst based on its power output. Drax is constantly developing new technologies in order to reduce their pollution levels and has had particular success in the reduction in sulphur emissions over the past five years.

Coal is unlikely ever to be a truly clean fuel. It will remain a core fuel for electricity production in many countries for several years to come. Any attempt to clean the emissions from coal fired power stations as a short term measure until new power stations can be built to replace coal is to be encouraged.

According to Drax themselves, the average CO_2 emissions for electricity generated at Drax Power Station during 2008 is 818g CO_2/kWh (1.79 pounds CO_2 per kWh). This figure has dropped from 840g CO_2/kWh (1.85 pounds CO_2 per kWh) in 2006. By the

---

[34] Union of Concerned Scientists: Environmental impacts of coal power.

[35] Drax Power Ltd Environmental Performance Review 2008.

end of 2011, Drax aim to achieve less than 700g CO_2/kWh (1.54 pounds CO_2 per kWh).

In the United States, the CO_2 emissions from coal fired power stations averages out at 990g CO_2 /kWh (2.18 pounds CO_2 per kWh).

Gas fired power stations

Natural gas fired power stations are the principle power generators in the UK, after significant investment by the Government in the 1980s and 1990s to move away from coal for economic reasons. In the UK, natural gas now accounts for 40% of the country's total energy needs.

Compared to coal, gas fired power stations have a significantly lower carbon footprint. In addition, the gas itself is usually piped directly to the gas station, which also reduces secondary carbon emissions as there is no transportation costs to get the fuel to the plants.

The switch from coal to gas in the UK was responsible for the significant drop in carbon emissions across the country during the 1990s.

Modern gas generated electricity has a carbon footprint of around 360g CO_2/kWh (0.88 pounds of CO_2 per kWh), although some of the older gas power stations (using 'open cycle' technology) have a carbon footprint of around 479g CO_2/kWh (1 pound of CO_2 per kWh).

Oil fired power stations

Oil fired power stations are often small power stations that are used to 'top up' the power grid when there is a high demand for power.

There are large oil fired power stations that are used for generating electricity from oil in the United States

They generate less pollution than coal fired power stations, but they are not as clean as gas fired power stations. They also generate more nitrogen oxide than coal fired power stations, which is regarded as a very significant greenhouse gas.

Nuclear power stations

Nuclear power stations generate very little air pollution. There is, however, radioactive waste created by nuclear power stations that has to be stored securely.

Nuclear power stations generate a constant level of energy and are often used as a 'base load' on the power grids, which are then supplemented by gas and coal fired power stations as demand rises.

France uses nuclear power stations to generate the vast majority of their electricity. Many other countries include nuclear in their general power mix.

Geo-thermal power stations

Geo-thermal energy is extracted from the heat stored deep inside the earth. Boreholes are drilled deep into the earth surface and water pumped in. Turbines are powered by the steam that is generated by the heat and in turn this generates electricity.

Iceland is the pioneer of geo-thermal energy. The country is on the boundaries between two tectonic plates in the earth's surface. The high concentration of volcanoes and hot water surface pools have made geo-thermal energy so cheap that in winter some of the pavements in the streets of major cities are heated.

Around one quarter of Iceland's electricity comes from geo-thermal energy. In addition, geo-thermal energy provides the heating and hot water needs for almost 90% of the buildings in the country.

Geo-thermal power stations are now being built and tested in different parts of the world, including in the United States, the United Kingdom and Canada.

Carbon dioxide emissions from geo-thermal power equate to around 122g CO_2/kWh (around 4½oz of CO_2 per kWh). Trace amounts of hydrogen sulphide, methane, ammonia, arsenic and mercury are also found and these are captured using emission control systems to filter this exhaust.

Hydro-electric power stations

Hydro-electricity is the most widely used form of 'renewable' energy. Once built, a hydro-electric power station produces no direct waste and has negligible emissions, although there may be environmental issues involved in the construction of hydro-electricity power stations.

20% of the world's electricity is generated by hydropower, which accounts for around 88% of all electricity from renewable sources.

Most hydro-electric power stations work by damming a river and creating a reservoir. The power comes from the potential energy of the water being driven downhill from the dam under pressure through a water turbine.

Very small scale hydro-electricity systems may also be powered by a water wheel.

Small scale hydro-electricity systems capable of producing anything from a few kW to around 10MW (megawatts) of power can be bought off-the-shelf from various manufacturers and can be installed at a suitable site within a few weeks. These have become popular in China where hundreds of 'micro-hydro' power stations have been installed in the past few years.

There are many benefits of hydro-electric power stations:

- There is no 'fuel', so there are few ongoing costs.
- Emissions are virtually eliminated.
- Hydro-electric power plants have a very long life. Many plants built 80-100 years ago are still in operation today.
- Power production can be increased and decreased at a turn of a tap, which makes them an extremely flexible source of power.

Many hydro-electric power stations have secondary uses. Some are used to manage water flow and stop flooding downstream, and others have become tourist attractions with the reservoirs being used for water sports and general recreation. I recently visited a hydro-electric power station in India that used the dam for irrigating rice fields around the area with a constant water supply.

Pumped Storage

The big issue with electricity production on a huge scale is that it is very difficult to store excess electricity when there is little demand and then use it when demand is at its highest.

This is going to become a bigger issue in the future with the introduction of more wind turbines that generate electricity based on the strength of the wind rather than based on demand.

Pumped Storage is a way of storing this excess energy and then releasing it on demand when required.

The system is based on hydro-electricity with a reservoir at the top of a hill and a second reservoir at the bottom.

During periods of excess electricity generation (typically in the middle of the night) water is pumped from the lower reservoir to the upper reservoir.

During periods of high demand, water is released back into the lower reservoir through a water turbine, generating electricity.

Many pumped storage systems have been built where there are two natural lakes. Others are built with man-made reservoirs. Pumped Storage plants are often built in combination with a standard hydro-electric power station.

Although Pumped Storage systems are ultimately a net user of electricity, they provide a way of storing excess energy extremely efficiently. Between 70%–85% of the electricity used to pump the water is regained when the water is released.

Like hydro-electric power stations, pumped storage has the huge benefit that they can provide electricity on demand. Quite literally, a pumped storage system can be turned on and off at a tap.

Wind Turbines

Wind power has been used for thousands of years, operating machinery to grind wheat or pump water or power farming equipment.

Using wind to generate electricity was first tested in Scotland in 1887 and wind turbine production in the United States started the following year. By 1908, there were 72 wind turbine electricity generators in use in the United States and by the 1930s they were a common sight on remote farms across the country.

Most wind turbines rotate on a horizontal axis and consist of between three and five blades, a gearbox and an electrical generator. The turbine has to face into the wind in order to generate electricity. Small generators are pointed using a wind vane. Large generators use electric motors to move the turbine head into the wind.

Wind turbines are best mounted at height and have to be installed where there is good airflow with minimal turbulence. Large turbines can generate between 2 and 6MW (megawatts) of power. This is enough to provide power between 2,000 and 6,000 homes.

Small wind turbines are available that are suitable for installing at homes or businesses. These typically generate between 0.5–6kW of electricity.

The big issue with wind turbines is they only generate electricity when the wind is blowing, rather than generating electricity on demand. For this reason they are difficult to integrate into a power grid. At best they can supplement electricity from other sources rather than replace it.

Solar

With a few exceptions, solar has yet to become a serious power generator on a scale to contribute useful amounts of power to a power grid.

There are exceptions. Solar farms have been built in Germany and Spain that provide between 1–10MW of power. Other schemes are being developed in Texas, California, Mexico and Tunisia.

A small amount of electricity can be generated from solar on an overcast day. The majority of the energy production comes on a sunny day. This can be a big benefit when the peak demands for electricity are on a sunny day – such as for running air conditioning units.

Solar is one of the best 'small scale' electricity generators available. If you require a relatively small amount of electricity at a location and there is no mains power available, solar is often the most cost effective and easiest energy production system to install and run.

Furthermore, quite a few electric car owners have installed their own solar 'power station' to generate electricity for running their electric car, ensuring their electric cars are truly 'green' vehicles.

Utility Grid Transmission Losses

As electricity is transmitted from the power stations to the consumers, a certain amount of energy is lost en route. These losses are reduced by transmitting electricity at very high voltages.

In the US, 7.2% of all energy generated is lost through utility grid transmission[36]. In the United Kingdom an average of 7% of all energy generated is lost through grid transmission[37].

Electric Cars and Electricity Supply

Critics claim that the power grid cannot provide enough electricity for electric cars without significant and costly upgrading.

It is true that if every combustion engine car was taken off the road and replaced with an electric one, electricity consumption would increase. It has been estimated that across the European Union, net electricity consumption would increase by 15%[38]. Worldwide, a total transport switch to electric vehicles would increase electricity consumption to 20%[39].

However, a complete 100% shift to electric power is extremely unlikely. Neither governments nor car manufacturers are anticipating a complete switch at any time over the next 40 years. Electricity companies and governments have investigated the likely

---

[36]US Climate Change Technology Program – Technology Options for the Near and Long Term, November 2003.

[37]Investigation into Transmission Losses on UK Electricity Transmission System. National Grid Technical Report. June 2008. / Electricity Distribution Losses – a Consultancy Document. Ofgem. January 2003.

[38]The future of transport in Europe: Electricity drives cleaner! Eurelectric (2009)

[39]Energy Technology Perspectives 2008: In support of the G8 plan of action. Scenarios and Strategies to 2050. IEA (2008).

power demand based on a number of different scenarios for electric car take-up. The results make interesting reading:

- In Germany, one million electric cars travelling an average of 10,000km a year would require less than one percent of its current electricity capacity in order to provide sufficient energy[40].

- Likewise, the UK Department for Transport claims that the UK has sufficient generating capacity to cope with the uptake of electric cars, assuming a managed charging cycle targeted at off-peak periods (particularly at night) when there is surplus capacity[41].

  The study carried out by the Department for Transport does suggest that if significant numbers of owners started charging their cars during peak hours, significant investment may be required in the longer term.

- In the United States, the American grid could support 94 million electric vehicles (43% of all cars on the road) if they were all charged during the evening and overnight, or 158 million vehicles (73% of all cars on the road) more advanced charging techniques currently being experimented with[42].

It is widely expected that the majority of electric cars will be charged up overnight, when there is surplus capacity and this will negate the need for investment in power upgrades. Power companies are likely to promote night time charging using smart metering (see page 130) and discounted energy tariffs.

In the course of writing this book, I have spoken at length with power network infrastructure specialists in the United Kingdom and France about the likely impact of electric cars on the power grid.

---

[40]The Electricification Approach to Urban Mobility and Transport. Strategy Paper. ERTRAC. 24th January 2009.

[41]Investigation into the scope for the transport sector to switch to electric vehicles and plug-in hybrid vehicles – United Kingdom Department for Transport (2008)

[42]Electric Powertrains: Opportunities and Challenges in the US light-duty vehicle fleet. Kromer and Heywood, Laboratory for Energy and the Environment, Massachusetts Institute of Technology.

There is widespread agreement that even a significant take up of electric cars is unlikely to cause problems in the next 10-15 years. In the longer term, there is an expectation that an emergence of fast charging stations and a substantial take up of electric cars may contribute to increased peak demand for electricity by 2025-2030.

Smart Metering

Smart Meters are the next generation of electricity and gas meters, providing customers (and energy suppliers) with accurate information about the amount of energy being consumed at any one time and the cost of that energy.

Smart Meters also allow energy suppliers to provide flexible tariffs to their customers so that electricity costs can be cheaper when demand is low and higher when demand is high. This offers the consumer the choice as to when they use their energy and encourages consumers to use energy as efficiently and as cost effectively as possible.

Many advanced Smart Metering systems can also be configured to switch appliances on and off depending on the cost of the energy.

In order to reduce the impact of electric cars on the power grid over the next few years, it is likely that electric car owners will be encouraged to install Smart Meters that automatically switch the cars on to charge when demand for electricity is low and therefore cheap.

Owners will be encouraged to charge their cars at night time with lower cost electricity, thereby reducing the impact of a large take-up of electric cars.

Monitoring the emissions of your own electric car

In the meantime, it is possible for you to monitor your own emissions of your electric car by monitoring the supply and demand on the power grid yourself.

The www.OwningElectricCar.com web site includes a data feed from the UK National Grid showing the power supply mix and average carbon footprint of the electricity being generated across the UK, updated every five minutes throughout the day. The site also recommends the best times of day to plug in your electric car based on electricity demand and carbon footprint.

It is planned that data from other countries will be added to the website as the data becomes available.

Fuel Economy

Finally, we now have a way of comparing the environmental performance for running an electric car compared to a petrol/gasoline or diesel powered car.

Using the information we now have, it is possible to measure the CO_2 emissions of an electric car and compare them with the CO_2 emissions of a combustion engine car.

Depending on the make and model, most electric cars can travel between 3½ and 7½ miles (6–12km) on a single kilowatt-hour of electricity.

In my chapter on *Electric Cars you can Drive Today* (starting on page 50), I include a list of all the electric cars that are available, along with the manufacturer supplied fuel economy figures expressed in the number of km you can travel on one kilowatt-hour of electricity (km/kWh).

Based on the carbon footprint of the electricity used to charge up the cars, we can therefore provide a 'well to wheel' carbon footprint for running an electric car.

Across the European Union, emission figures for cars are shown as the number of grams of CO_2 generated in a single km of driving (g CO_2/km).

There is currently not a direct equivalent of this in North America. However, as many of the cars sold in Europe are also available in North America, these comparative figures are available and allow you to measure how environmentally efficient a combustion engine car is compared to an electric car.

For these reasons, I am showing these comparative figures in metric measurements. If you want to work in pounds and ounces, one ounce is 28g and one pound is 454g.

	Grams of CO_2 per km						
	6km	7km	8km	9km	10km	11km	12km
Austria 221g/kWh	37g	31½g	27½g	24½g	22g	20g	18½g
Australia 936g/kWh	156g	134g	117g	104g	93½g	85g	78g
Canada 234g/kWh	39g	33½g	29g	26g	23½g	21g	19½g
Denmark 308g/kWh	51½g	44g	38½g	34g	31g	28g	26g
France 87g/kWh	14½g	12½g	11g	10g	9g	8g	7g
Germany 453g/kWh	75½g	64½g	56½g	50½g	45½g	41g	38g
Iceland 138g/kWh	23g	20g	17g	15½g	14g	12½g	11½g
India 930g/kWh	155g	133g	116g	103g	93g	84½g	77½g
Ireland 573g/kWh	95½g	82g	72g	63½g	57½g	52g	48g
Japan 429g/kWh	71½g	61½g	53½g	47½g	42½g	39g	38g
Nepal 1g/kWh	>¼g	>¼g	>¼g	>¼g	0.1g	Trace	Trace
New Zealand 275g/kWh	46g	39g	34½g	30½g	27½g	25g	23g
Norway 7g/kWh	1g	1g	1g	1g	½g	½g	½g
Pakistan 380g/kWh	63½g	54½g	47½	42g	38g	34½g	31½g
UK 537g/kWh	89½g	77½g	67g	60g	54g	49g	45g
USA 609g/kWh	101½g	87g	76g	67½g	61g	55½g	51g

As you can see, there is a huge difference in CO_2 emissions depending on which country you live in. If you live in Norway or Nepal where most of the electricity is generated with hydro power, your CO_2 emissions are virtually zero if you drive an electric car.

In countries, such as Australia and India, this chart suggests there is only a small benefit of an electric car over an equivalent combustion engine car. In reality, there is a saving once 'well to wheel' emissions for combustion engine cars are taken into account.

I demonstrate this in my chapter on real world economy tests, starting on page 143.

As there is wild variation between CO_2 emissions in each country, it is not possible to provide a blanket CO_2 per km measurement. It is, however, possible to create this measurement by country:

Make and Model	Canada CO_2	France CO_2	India CO_2	UK CO_2	USA CO_2
Aixam Mega City	29g/km	11g/km	116g/km	67g/km	76g/km
Mitsubishi i-MiEV	24g/km	9g/km	93g/km	54g/km	61g/km
Nissan LEAF[43]	33g/km	12g/km	133g/km	77g/km	87g/km
REVA/G-Wiz L-ion	21g/km	8g/km	84g/km	49g/km	56g/km

How to further improve an electric cars CO_2 footprint

In countries where there is a comprehensive mix of different power generation sources, high carbon sources of electricity production such as coal fired power stations are often put on standby when electricity demand is low. Instead, electricity is typically generated by nuclear and hydro power stations.

---

[43]Estimated figures based on 100 mile (160km) range: Nissan were unable to provide actual economy figures.

In the UK, where the national power grid provides detailed power information every five minutes throughout the day, it is possible to identify how much power is being produced and what the power source is, as it is being used.

Based on this information, you can quickly identify the best time to charge your electric car in order to reduce your carbon footprint. In the UK, the carbon footprint for a kilowatt-hour of electricity varies from around 290-350g/kW during the night, up to 550-600g/kW during the late afternoon.

In almost every country in the world, the carbon footprint of the electricity supply falls between 11pm and 7am. If you can charge up your car between those times, your carbon footprint for using your electric car will be lower than if you charge up at any other time.

Carbon footprints for charging an electric car at different times in the UK:

Make and Model	UK Average (537g/kWh)	UK overnight (330g/kWh)	UK peak – early evening (600g/kWh)
Aixam Mega City	67g/km	41g/km	75g/km
Mitsubishi i-MiEV	54g/km	33g/km	60g/km
Nissan LEAF[44]	77g/km	47g/km	85g/km
REVA/G-Wiz L-ion	49g/km	30g/km	54g/km

This chart shows that there is a significant difference in the carbon footprint of an electric car, depending on the time of day that the car is charged.

You can monitor the UK power grid using the website that accompanies this book:

http://www.OwningElectricCar.com

Other countries will be added over the coming months.

---

[44]Estimated figures based on 100 mile (160km) range: Nissan were unable to provide actual economy figures at the time of writing.

Fuel economy for combustion engine cars

By way of a comparison, here are published manufacturers figures for some of the most efficient petrol/gasoline and diesel powered cars currently on sale today, shown as 'tank to wheel' CO_2 figures.

Alongside them, I have shown an estimated 'well to wheel' figure based on the CO_2 impact of producing the fuel in the first place (based on the figures and calculations shown on page 118) by multiplying the tank to wheel figure by 1.205:

Make and Model	'Tank to Wheel' CO_2 figures	'Well to Wheel' CO_2 figures
Chevrolet Aveo	132g/km	159g/km
Ford Fiesta ECOtec (diesel)	98g/km	118g/km
Honda Insight	101g/km	122g/km
MINI Cooper Diesel	103g/km	124g/km
Nissan Pixo 1.0	103g/km	124g/km
Smart ForTwo (diesel)	88g/km	106g/km
Smart ForTwo 52kW	103g/km	124g/km
Toyota Aygo	106g/km	127g/km
Toyota IQ 1.0 VVTi	99g/km	119g/km
Toyota Prius (2010 model)	89g/km	107g/km
Volkswagen Polo Bluemotion	99g/km	119g/km
Volvo V30 1.6D DRIVe	99g/km	119g/km

If you compare these figures with the electric car figures shown on page 133, you will see that electric cars provide significantly lower 'well to wheel' emissions than combustion engine cars in almost every country in the world.

Real world testing

As part of the research for this book, I undertook my own tests to measure real world carbon emissions of both electric cars and combustion engine cars, driving on a variety of roads.

You can read the results of these tests starting on page 143.

The environmental impact of batteries

It is important to measure the environmental impact of batteries (both their construction and what happens at the end of their life) when considering an electric car.

There are two main battery technologies that are now used in electric cars. Lead acid batteries are used in smaller, lower powered vehicles. Larger and more powerful vehicles are now using lithium-ion batteries.

Nickel Metal Hydride batteries (as used in the Toyota Prius) are now rarely used in full electric vehicles.

Lead acid batteries will need to be replaced several times during the life of the vehicle. Depending on the exact technology used, lithium-ion batteries may require replacement once during the lifetime of the car, although some manufacturers, like Mitsubishi, expect the batteries on their electric cars to last the lifetime of the vehicle.

In order to provide a comparison between the different batteries, I am going to assume that a car has a lifespan of 12 years. If the car uses lead acid batteries, I am going to assume that during this time it will drive 50,000 miles (80,000km). If the car uses lithium-ion batteries, I am going to assume that during the car lifetime, it will drive 100,000 miles (160,000km).

We can then use these figures to come up with an approximate CO_2/km figure for the environmental impact of the batteries used in an electric car.

I've assumed two different distances because of the different characteristics of the different batteries:

- Lead acid batteries are typically used in small, speed restricted electric vehicles that are more appropriate for town or city use.

- Lithium-ion batteries are much lighter and more powerful and are typically used in faster and longer range electric cars.

Lead Acid batteries

Lead acid batteries are the mainstay of the electric car industry at present. It is easy to see why. They provide a reliable source of power at a comparatively low cost and they are simple batteries to integrate into a vehicle.

The disadvantage of lead acid batteries is that they have a typical lifespan of only three years. At the end of their life they need to be disposed of.

A typical electric car equipped with lead acid batteries will have between 8-12 batteries, providing a total of 8-12kWh of energy storage.

Lead acid batteries are a simple technology that is cheap and easy to manufacture. Their cases are typically made of polypropylene, the plates are made of lead and a mixture of acid and water is used as an electrolyte.

Many lead acid batteries also have a very high percentage of reused materials.

As a consequence, the carbon cost of manufacture is low. Around 15kg of CO_2 is generated through a build of a typical 1kWh lead acid battery.[45]

Thanks to the value of the raw materials, there is an active market in recycling lead acid batteries at the end of their lives. In Europe, virtually 100% of all lead acid batteries are recycled and in the United States, the figure is around 98%.

97% of a lead acid battery can be recycled. The casing can be melted down and reformed. Lead has a low melting point, and as a consequence it requires very little energy to be converted back into a raw material and reused.[46]

Lead acid batteries are typically recycled to produce new lead acid batteries, thereby keeping the carbon footprint down for the next generation of lead acid batteries.

Based on an electric vehicle requiring eight lead acid batteries which are then replaced every three years, the carbon footprint for

---

[45]Source: HGI: How Green is a Lead Acid Battery? A study of the environmental impact of the lead acid battery.

[46]Source: International Lead Association: fact sheet on lead recycling.

the batteries in an electric car, spread over the lifetime of the vehicle is as follows:

Estimated carbon footprint per battery:	15kg
Estimated carbon footprint per battery pack (8 batteries):	120kg
Estimated number of battery packs needed during the lifetime of the vehicle:	4
Carbon footprint over lifetime of vehicle:	480kg
CO_2/km based on 50,000 miles (80,000km)	6g

Examples of vehicles with this configuration include the REVA i (G-Wiz), the Aixam Mega City and most NEVs.

Lithium Ion

Lithium Ion batteries have a significantly longer lifespan than lead acid batteries. Some lithium ion batteries have a lifespan of 5-7 years. Other manufacturers are using a much more expensive battery technology that is designed to last the lifetime of the vehicle.

The carbon cost for manufacturing a typical lithium ion battery pack for a car is around 22kg for every 1 kWh of energy storage[47]. Most small electric cars with lithium ion batteries have between 12–16 kWh of batteries. This gives an equivalent carbon footprint of between 264kg and 352kg per vehicle.

When lithium ion batteries reach the end of their useful lives, the metals from the batteries can be extracted. At present, around 50% of the materials from the batteries can be recovered and reused for making new batteries. By 2015, it is anticipated these figures will be up to 95%.

It has been calculated that new lithium ion batteries produced from recovered lithium will have a manufacturing carbon footprint of around 6.8kg per kWh of energy storage.[48]

---

[47]Source: Umicore, based on the CO_2 emissions of Saft Li-Ion MP 176065 cells.

[48]Source: Umicore: Strategic choices in Li-Ion and NiMH battery recycling.

Estimated carbon footprint for a
    12kWh battery pack: 220kg
Carbon footprint over lifetime of vehicle[49]:   440kg
CO_2/km based on 100,000 miles (160,000km)   3g

The environmental impact of vehicle manufacturing and distribution

In the United Kingdom, the Society for Motor Manufacturers and Traders (SMMT) estimated in 2005 the energy needed to manufacture a car in the United Kingdom translated to 600kg of CO_2, down from an estimated 1,100kg in 1999. In addition to these figures, the SMMT estimated the production of the raw materials is added a further 450kg per vehicle.

In the United States, Honda estimates their average to be 810kg of CO_2. At time of writing, they do not have any estimates for the raw material impact.

More recently, Kia carried out a total lifecycle analysis assessment of their forthcoming Cadenza mid-range car, measuring the carbon footprint of the car from the point of manufacture to the point of destruction. The work was certified by the Korea Environmental Industry and Technology Institute (KEITI).

According to their figures, production of the raw materials for the Kia Cadenza causes the emission of 3.48 tons of carbon dioxide. A further 0.531 tons are produced in the production of the car and 0.012 tons during recycling[50]. These figures are dwarfed by the carbon dioxide emissions from actually using the car: 25.5 tons of carbon dioxide emissions based on 75,000 miles (120,000km) of driving.

Electric vehicle manufacturer REVA is currently building a new state-of-the-environment production facility, constructed to

---

[49]Based on an electric car requiring eight lead acid batteries, replacing them every three years. Examples of cars with this configuration include the REVA i (G-Wiz), all GEM cars and the Aixam Mega City.

[50]Source: Hyun-jin Cho, Sustainability Manger, Kia Motors.

platinum level LEED[51] Green Building certification. The site includes rainwater harvesting, solar energy and CO_2 monitoring facilities. Electric buses will be used to transport workers to and from work.

REVA believe their carbon footprint for an electric car will be significantly lower than the carbon footprint for other cars and not just because of their state-of-the-art factory. REVA claim electric cars use around 80% fewer parts than conventional cars, ensuring they have a very low carbon footprint.

At time of writing, they are still working to ascertain the exact carbon footprint of their vehicles and have not been able to provide me with the exact information as to their carbon footprint.

However, from mid 2010, REVA is planning to publish the carbon footprint of all their cars. Where it is not possible to reduce the carbon footprint of the car, REVA say the footprint will be offset using carbon offsetting schemes.

International Shipping

In terms of environmental impact, it makes very little difference as to whether your car was shipped around the world from the factory to the customer, or whether it was built a few miles down the road. Less than 1% of the overall carbon footprint of the average vehicle is associated with distribution[52]. International shipping makes up the smallest part of the carbon footprint associated with distribution.

A far higher part of the footprint associated with vehicle distribution is attributed to the road transportation of the car.

The environmental impact of vehicle recycling

Car manufacturers and governments alike have worked hard on ensuring that when cars come to the end of their lives, as much of it as possible can be recycled.

---

[51]LEED – Leadership in Energy and Environmental Design: an internationally accepted rating system and benchmark for evaluating and certifying sustainable sites.

[52]Ecolane Transport Consultancy: Life Cycle Assessment of Vehicle Fuels and Technologies – March 2006.

Most car manufacturers already go further. Since the early 1980s, Mercedes Benz has been using recycled materials in the production of their cars and today most cars have a proportion of recycled materials in their build.

Across Europe, every post-1980 car that is scrapped at the end of its life must be recycled, with a minimum of 85% of its content reused.

Car manufacturers are now legally responsible for ensuring cars they manufactured are properly recycled at the end of their life and in the vast majority of cases, well over 90% of the content of a scrapped car is now reused through vehicle recycling.

It is too early to say whether an electric car is more or less recyclable than any other type of car. It is unlikely, however, that it will be too different from existing vehicle recycling. Battery recycling is already well established and the high value of the metals used in both the batteries and the motor in an electric car will ensure it is financially profitable for vehicle recyclers to recycle electric cars properly.

Chapter Summary

Buying and running an electric car has significant environmental benefits over any other type of car:

- The carbon footprint associated with electric car production is less than other vehicles.

- The carbon footprint associated with driving an electric car is less than other vehicles, even when battery replacement and recycling is taken into account.

- The issues that used to exist with recycling lithium batteries have been addressed and are improving year on year. By the time electric cars that are built now are being recycled, it is expected that between 95-97% of all lithium will be recoverable from a lithium battery.

Could electric cars speed up climate change?

The European Federation for Transport and Environment recently wrote a report for EU policy makers called 'How to avoid an electric shock: Electric cars – from hype to reality'. If you are a policymaker anywhere in the world who is looking at electric vehicles, you should read this report.

Published in November 2009, the report gained widespread attention from around the world where it was claimed that plug in electric cars could speed up climate change and increase carbon dioxide emissions.

The story was picked up by the press and many journalists twisted the story to say that electric cars were 'bad for the environment'.

The headline was taken out of context. What the report actually highlighted were two issues with the EU Emissions Trading Scheme (ETS).

The first issue the report highlighted is the Emissions Trading Scheme allows car manufacturers to rate electric cars as zero CO_2 polluters, when in fact pollution is created through electricity generation.

The second issue highlighted in the report is that the scheme allows car manufacturers to offset double the amount of CO2 emissions from other cars for every electric car they sell until the end of 2015.

As a consequence, manufacturers who build both electric cars and combustion engine cars can more easily reach the mandatory average CO_2 emissions of 130g CO_2/km by 2015, where the real world CO_2 emissions are actually significantly higher.

What is being appraised is the ETS policy, rather than electric cars themselves. The report argues that industry and policymakers have relied in the past on distant 'dream' technologies to solve environmental problems rather than setting targets for CO2 emissions and fuel efficiency. Hydrogen and bio fuels, have come to nothing for different reasons but what they have in common is that they all distracted policymakers from forcing carmakers to improve fuel efficiency across the board.

The report also examines the implications of electric cars for the power sector. It argues that the EU needs to think hard about how it will ensure that the extra demand for electricity is met through renewable electricity and not more dirty coal.

Over the next two to three years these issues will be theoretical as the volume of electric cars sold will be small. By the end of the decade, however, these concerns have the potential to be significant issues unless they are addressed.

It is up to EU policy makers to rectify this issue. Thanks to this report, it is likely there will be a change in the policy.

Incidentally, this is only an issue with manufacturers who build both electric cars and combustion engine cars. Buying a car from a manufacturer who only builds electric cars such as REVA or BYD, for instance, ensures that your car makes a genuine contribution to a global reduction in CO_2 emissions.

REAL WORLD ECONOMY FIGURES FOR ELECTRIC CARS

In the real world, with real world driving, it seems virtually impossible to get the fuel economy figures that the manufacturers claim for their models. Whether you're talking about combustion engine cars or electric cars, the figures appear to have little relevance in the real world other than to work as a comparison with other makes and models.

In an electric car, however, you can create your own fuel economy measurements extremely easily. Simply record your distance travelled and then measure the amount of electricity used to recharge the car using a plug in watt meter.

The test

In order to measure 'real world' economy for electric cars, I carried out a driving test along a fixed route with two different electric cars.

In order to provide a useful comparison, I then tested two combustion engine cars, driving the same route in order to identify real world fuel economy and comparative carbon footprint figures for each type of vehicle.

I decided to use my own personal commute to and from work as a test route, travelling in busy traffic. The distance travelled is 7 miles (approximately 11¼km) each way. The route comprises of 2½ miles (4 km) of fast freeways and 4½ miles (7¼ km) of busy inner city roads.

The tests were carried out in and around Coventry in the United Kingdom in January 2010. Temperatures were around freezing during the whole trial. Cabin heating was used as appropriate.

Noting the temperature is important. Electric cars are less economical in cold conditions than they are in hot conditions. These tests therefore reflect a 'worse case' economy for electric cars. In warmer conditions, it would be fair to expect significantly improved figures on an electric car.

Likewise in cold conditions, combustion engine cars take longer to warm up and are also not at their most economical at the start of their journey.

The economy of all vehicles could be expected to improve in warmer conditions. The tests will be repeated in the summer of 2010. The information for this summer test will be published on the website and in the 2011 edition of this book.

Test validity

It is worth stressing that these tests have not been independently verified by any scientific establishment. Consequently, these tests can only ever be used as an indication of relative fuel economy and carbon emissions.

I have also felt that it is important that my test could be repeated by anyone else using their own cars and their own routes.

All the information and calculations I used in order to carry out my tests are included within this chapter. If a university or a scientific establishment wish to carry out similar tests in a controlled environment and would like to talk to me about my test methods, I can be contacted through the *Ask me a Question* page of www.OwningElectricCar.com.

The electric cars

Two electric cars were chosen: a brand new Mitsubishi i-MiEV and a three year old REVA G-Wiz dc-drive with old batteries.

The Mitsubishi was chosen as an excellent example of the latest technology electric car. It is a sub-compact car with a roomy interior providing good performance and range.

The REVA dc-drive was chosen to identify whether an electric vehicle remains environmentally efficient as the batteries degrade and the car gets older. The REVA dc-drive is no longer on sale, it has been replaced by the more efficient REVA *i* and REVA L-ion. It represents a good test on an older electric car.

At midnight each night, each car was plugged in until the battery packs were completely charged. The amount of electricity used was monitored using a watt meter and this was then multiplied by the average carbon footprint for UK electricity during the period the cars were on charge. I was charging the cars overnight when the power grids are under-used and the carbon footprint averaged out at 330g/kWh.

This carbon footprint figure takes into account the carbon impact of sourcing the fuel and transporting it to the power station, the production of the power and the average transmission losses of the power as it is delivered from the power station to the car.

You can view these figures yourself on the *How green is the Grid?* web page on www.OwningElectricCar.com.

I also recalculated the carbon footprint figures based on the environmental footprint of a coal-fired power station using the US average carbon figures of 990g/kWh.

Finally, I took into account a carbon footprint for the use of the batteries, as shown on page 136.

The combustion engine cars

The combustion engine cars chosen were a brand new Toyota Aygo and a 2007 model Fiat Panda.

Both of these cars are economical sub-compact city cars that produce low levels of carbon emissions. The manufacturers own CO_2 footprint figures show that in official tests, the Toyota Aygo produces a 'tank to wheel' footprint of 106g CO_2/km, whilst the Fiat Panda produces a 'tank to wheel' footprint of 119g CO_2/km.

These figures only reflect the 'tank to wheel' emissions, not the 'well to wheel' emissions. For our tests to be comparative to the electric car tests, well to wheel calculations have to be used.

In order to calculate the carbon footprint in real conditions, I filled the fuel tank at the start of the test. I then measured the fuel economy in litres at the end of each test by refilling the fuel tank. I calculated the CO_2 footprint based on the amount of fuel used, using the 'well to wheel' CO_2 figures shown on page 118.

Test results from the electric cars:

	i-MiEV	GWiz
Distance Travelled	14.1 miles	14.1 miles
	22.56 km	22.56 km
Electricity Used	3,190 watts	2,990 watts
Total electricity cost[53]	26p UK	24p UK
	31¢ US	30¢ US
Average CO$_2$ per kWh	330g/kWh	330g/kWh
CO$_2$/km electricity usage	46.66 g/km	43.73 g/km
CO$_2$/km battery usage[54]	3g/km	6g/km
Total CO$_2$/km	**49.66 g/km**	**49.73 g/km**

These figures show remarkable fuel economies and a low recharge cost for the electric cars. The carbon footprint is also low, which is helped by using off-peak electricity. Off peak electricity is much more carbon friendly than using electricity during peak times.

What if they were powered by coal?

When electric cars are powered by coal fired power stations, the carbon footprint is significantly higher than when they are powered by most other sources.

Using the US figures of 990g/kWh for coal fired power, this is what the CO$_2$/km would look like if I charged up using coal power:

	i-MiEV	GWiz
CO$_2$/km electricity usage based on coal power	139.98 g/km	131.21 g/km

---

[53] Costs based on a night time tariff of 8p per unit in the UK, and 10¢ per unit in the United States.

[54] See the section on the Environmental Impact on Batteries on page 130 for a definition for this figure.

Test results from the combustion engine cars

	Toyota Aygo	Fiat Panda
Distance Travelled	14.1 miles 22.56 km	14.1 miles 22.56 km
Fuel Used	1.33 litres	1.51 litres
Total Fuel Cost[55]	£1.52 UK 92¢ US	£1.73 UK $1.04 US
Official CO_2/km tank to wheel	106g/km	119g/km
Actual CO_2/km tank to wheel	136.48 g/km	154.94 g/km
CO_2/km well to wheel	**164.46 g/km**	**186.70 g/km**

As you can see, the carbon footprint figures that I achieved in my test are significantly higher than the official CO_2 figures. There are various reasons for this:

- The cars were driven by me and not a professional test driver. Whilst I did use eco-driving techniques, I would never claim to be the best eco-driver in the world!

- The tests started with cold engines in cold conditions.

- The cars were driven on a variety of roads, including freeways, sub-urban roads and city streets in heavy traffic conditions.

- Cabin heating was used in the cars as appropriate to keep the windscreen clear (this is also true of the electric cars).

---

[55] Fuel price based on a UK cost of £1.14 per litre and a US cost of $2.60 per US gallon.

Side by side analysis: well to wheel measurements

	Mitsubishi i-MiEV	REVA GWiz	Toyota Aygo	Fiat Panda
Fuel Cost	26p UK 31¢ US	24p UK 30¢ US	£1.52 UK 92¢ US	£1.73 UK 69¢ US
CO_2/km	46.66 g/km	43.73 g/km	164.46 g/km	186.70 g/km

Side by side analysis if powered by coal

If the electric cars had been powered by a coal-fired power station, the carbon footprint comparison would look like this:

	Mitsubishi i-MiEV	REVA GWiz	Toyota Aygo	Fiat Panda
CO_2/km	139.98 g/km	131.21 g/km	164.46 g/km	186.70 g/km

Chapter Summary

- I have carried out tests on the comparative economies of two different electric cars and two economical combustion engine cars.

- As these tests have not been independently verified, they can only ever be used as an indication of relative fuel economy and carbon emissions.

- The tests indicate that electric cars are significantly better for the environment than the equivalent combustion engine car.

- Even if my electricity is generated by a coal-fired power station, my tests indicate that an electric car is still better for the environment than a combustion engine car.

A FINAL WORD

Electric cars are radically different and an exciting new technology that have practical uses in our daily lives and have significant environmental and economic benefits.

For many people they are the ideal vehicle, providing quiet, smooth and practical motoring for the new decade.

If, through the pages of this book, I've encouraged you to go out and try an electric car, or even better given you the confidence to get one for yourself, I have achieved what I set out to do.

Likewise, if you have read the book and come to the conclusion that an electric car is not suitable for you, this book has also served its purpose. Far better to spend a small amount of money buying a book than spend a lot of money on buying the wrong car.

The electric car industry is a very exciting one and over the next few years there will be some very significant new developments. For this reason, I will be producing regular updates to this book in order to keep up with the latest technology, ideas and products.

Finally, if you've enjoyed this book, or even if you haven't, feel free to get in touch. If you have questions about electric cars, or suggestions on how I can improve the book, I would be delighted to hear from you.

I can be contacted through the 'Ask me a Question' page on my website www.OwningElectricCar.com.

All the best,

Michael Boxwell
January 2010

G-Wiz!

Unlikely as it may seem, this little electric city car started a revolution

In early 2004, a tiny new car appeared on the streets of London, confusing and surprising everyone who saw it: more compact than a Smart, it had cheeky quirky styling and travelled in silence.

The car attracted attention wherever it went. What was it? Who made it? Why is it so quiet? Suddenly, the media were falling over each other to report on a new type of vehicle... the G-Wiz.

In a remarkably short period of time, the little G-Wiz went from being an unknown to a media sensation. TV celebrities, Hollywood stars, politicians and captains of industry were queuing up to buy them; fashion designers created special editions. Against all the odds, the G-Wiz became cool.

Hundreds of people flocked to buy a G-Wiz. Some were attracted by the cheap running costs and exemption from London's 'Congestion Charge' tax and free parking. Others were attracted by its environmental credentials. Lots were bought by SUV owners, wanting a smaller car to use in the city.

Local government responded by installing charging points and offering free parking in many parts of the city.

Other car makers watched in astonishment. Why were people buying a simple electric car over their own far superior models? Why was there a five month waiting list for the G-Wiz? It was the first indication that the general public was eager to buy electric cars.

Honda and Peugeot showed electric concept cars of similar dimensions to the G-Wiz. Norbert Reithofer, CEO at BMW started openly talking about BMW building "a G-Wiz competitor".

Few cars have divided opinion, or created as much debate as the G-Wiz. Few cars are likely ever to do so again.

Today, six years after London saw its first G-Wiz, it remains popular – visit a car park in the City of London or City of Westminster and you'll see more G-Wiz than any other single model of car.

A recent Frost and Sullivan survey into electric vehicles noted that when people find out about electric cars, their interest in buying one doubles. I carried out a survey with car users as research for this book: in cities where the G-Wiz is common, people are twice as likely to consider buying an electric car.

Each day, the G-Wiz demonstrates to millions of Londoners that electric cars are practical – for the first time in 100 years. It's a legacy that will live on for a very long time.

APPENDIX A: A BRIEF HISTORY OF ELECTRIC CARS

Electric cars are nothing new. In fact they pre-date Karl Benz's infamous 1886 tricycle. Somewhere between 1832 and 1839, Scottish inventor Robert Anderson built a very simple electric carriage and American Thomas Davenport built an electric road vehicle in 1842.

The first vehicles were experimental only. The rechargeable batteries were not available until later in the 19th Century, with the first commercially available rechargeable batteries that were suitable for electric cars becoming available in 1881.

The first production electric car was built in London in 1884 by Thomas Parker, a British inventor who was also responsible for electrifying the London Underground.

Figure 8 - the 1888 Electric Rover.

Early electric cars quickly established a reputation for performance, reliability and distance that it could travel. In comparison, the internal combustion engine was noisy, smelly and unreliable and had limited power. They had to be hand cranked to start them, which was dangerous and led to many injuries, fuel efficiency was poor and the fuel itself was not easily available.

The first world land speed record was set in an electric car on the 18th December, 1898. Count Gaston de Chasseloup-Laubat set the record in a Jentaud automobile powered by alkaline batteries, reaching a top speed of 39.245mph (62.792km/h) in Acheres Park, near Paris. Four months later, Camile Jenatzy drove another electric car – *Le Jamais Contende* – to a new world record, reaching 65.79mph (105.264km/h).

By the turn of the 20th Century, electric cars were outselling gasoline cars. In New York, Paris and London, electric taxis had appeared and electric cars were liked because they were reliable, did not smell, vibrate or make noise and they were easy to drive.

At the turn of the century, all cars were 'horseless carriages' and they were used as direct replacements for the horse and cart. Car journeys were short, lasting no more than a few miles at most. Roads out of town were little more than mud tracks: if you wanted to travel further afield, you took the train. In such an environment, it is no wonder that electric cars were popular.

Electric cars proved to be exceptionally reliable, too. This was an era where an engine needed to be rebuilt every 500 miles. Electric cars could continue for the whole of their working lives with very little maintenance. There was at least one instance of an electric taxi in London that covered 180,000 miles over a period of ten years – an unheard of distance at that time.

In Europe, electric cars continued to be popular until the outbreak of the First World War in 1914. By the time the war had finished in 1918, gasoline cars were vastly more reliable, petroleum was significantly cheaper and more easily available and thanks to Henry Ford's new mass production techniques, gasoline cars were far cheaper to buy than electric cars. Service stations and fuel pumps were appearing, making it easier to buy fuel. New roads linking one town to another were being built enabling longer distance travelling. It was the end of an era. The electric car was dead and the combustion engine was king.

Electric vehicles did not entirely disappear. In the United Kingdom, electric delivery vans had found a niche with home delivery companies. Electric delivery vans became popular with companies like Harrods and with milk delivery companies ('milk floats'). By the early 1960s, over 60,000 electric delivery vans were in daily use in the United Kingdom. The traditional home delivery market went into decline in the 1970s and 1980s and the electric commercial vehicle market collapsed. Today, there are still around 12,000 'milk floats' on the roads. A significant number of these vans were originally built in the 1960s or 1970s and very few are less than 20 years old.

The oil crisis in the early 1970s saw manufacturers planning a new era for electric cars. Ford, General Motors and AMC all produced a number of concepts and prototypes. Smaller companies such as Sebring-Vanguard and Elcar Corp in the United States and Enfield in Europe produced and sold small two-seater electric city cars, a number of which are still in use today and have an enthusiastic following from their owners.

From that time onwards, however, the electric car quietly faded off the scene. In Europe, Fiat and Volkswagen both built a handful of cars in the 1980s but the cost was too high and there was little or no public interest in them. Petrol was comparatively cheap and there seemed no incentive to change.

Interest in electric cars only resurfaced in the mid-1990s, when concerns about the environment and climate change became a factor.

In the California, the California Air Resources Board passed a ruling called the Low Emission Vehicle Program in 1990, which was enacted by the Californian government to promote the use of zero emission vehicles. The law stated that 2% of all new vehicles sold in California were to be zero emission vehicles by 1998, rising to 10% of all new vehicles by 2003.

Across America, car makers developed new electric vehicles in order to comply with the new law. General Motors launched the EV1 electric sedan, Ford launched an electric version of its Explorer SUV and bought TH!NK, a Norwegian electric car manufacturer, Chrysler bought electric car maker GEM, Toyota produced an electric RAV-4 and Honda produced a small city car.

All the manufacturers offered their cars to the public through lease schemes rather than outright purchase. Technical problems dogged the EV1 and although owners were enthusiastic about their new cars, high leasing costs meant they were not good sellers. The cars sold in tiny numbers.

Changes to the Low Emission Vehicle Program meant that manufacturers did not need to sell electric vehicles in California and at the end of their leases, most of the cars were taken back by the manufacturers and many of them were crushed.

In Europe, Peugeot, Citroen and Renault started building electric versions of their small city cars. The Renault soon fell by the wayside but Peugeot and Citroen manufactured a range of small commercial vehicles and city cars. Public interest was still low, however and sales were below expectation. First production of the city cars ceased in 2003, followed by the small electric delivery vans in 2006. Ironically, this was the exact time when resurgence in interest in electric vehicles was showing an upturn in sales.

In India, a tiny and unheard of new company was preparing to launch its new electric city car. Called 'REVA', the new car had quirky styling, could seat two adults and two small children and had a range of around 40 miles and a top speed of 40mph.

The car sold in India in small numbers for the first few years. Then, in mid-2003, a British company called GoinGreen imported a few cars and branded them as 'G-Wiz'.

The original idea of renting them out to commuters in Leeds floundered and the company moved to London in 2004.

At the same time, London was reeling from a new congestion charge tax. If you wanted to drive in London during the day, you had to pay a £5 ($8) fee. Electric cars were exempt from the new charge.

The first G-Wiz appeared in London early in 2004. Taking Londoners by surprise, the car was an instant hit. Electric car charging points were installed in car parks and on streets and London became seen as the 'Electric Car Capital' of the world.

Meanwhile, the awareness of global warming was increasing and Governments and politicians were increasingly viewing pollution from transportation as a major issue to be tackled.

Increasingly, the discussions between governments and car makers revolved around making cars cleaner and more fuel efficient. From the middle of the decade, electric cars came up on the agenda more and more often. Car makers started work on electric car research and started showing electric car concepts at motor shows.

Meanwhile, smaller manufacturers were launching new electric cars. NEVs were slowly gaining momentum in the United States, electric quadricycles were becoming popular in London, Paris, Rome, Bangalore, Delhi and Shanghai.

The Tesla electric sports car, originally announced in 2007, grabbed a huge amount of attention for electric cars. Here was a compact, fast, two seat sports car that looked and drove like a Ferrari and had a range of hundreds of miles. Public interest was growing and it wasn't long before Tesla's order books were full.

By 2010, mainstream manufacturers were joining the party. Mitsubishi was first with the i-MiEV – a four seat, four door city car now available in Japan and the United Kingdom. Ford and Nissan have cars being launched during 2010 and most manufacturers have an EV under development for launch in the next two years.

Incredibly, the history of electric cars stretches back around 175 years. Yet only now can it be said that 'the car of tomorrow' has finally arrived.

Learning the lessons from history

History tells us that electric cars have been successful only when they have been economically viable. Electric cars were successful at the dawn of the motoring era but fell from grace as combustion engine technology improved and the costs for building combustion engine cars reduced to the point that electric cars were over twice the price of the equivalent combustion engine cars.

Interest in electric vehicles rises when oil prices increase dramatically and fall when oil is cheap. The oil crisis of the early 1970s created a new market for electric cars but by the time these were on the market the crisis was over. The higher purchase price of these electric vehicles meant they were unviable and quickly faded away.

In the mid-1990s, a number of car manufacturers produced electric versions of their cars. Ford, Toyota, Renault, Citroen and Peugeot all launched electric motor versions of existing cars. General Motors and Honda built new cars from scratch.

In Europe, where these cars were sold rather than leased, the high purchase price meant that car sales were negligible. Electric cars could not make a financial case for themselves. In the United States, where cars were leased rather than sold, the high lease cost put off many people.

The first electric car to become a success was the G-Wiz. The car was successful because it was economically viable and was comparable in cost to other small city cars.

Other small electric cars launched since have sold in tiny numbers in comparison. The reason? The purchase price is too high and therefore the cost cannot be compared with a conventional city car.

The general public do express an interest in owning electric cars. In a recent survey carried out by Frost and Sullivan[56], 14% of consumers across Europe said they were likely or very likely to consider purchasing an electric vehicle for their next vehicle purchase.

However, when shown the likely price of an electric vehicle, this interest rapidly disappears. According to the research, the high price of many electric vehicles will be an inhibiting factor for adoption. The average price across Europe that people would be prepared to pay for a family sized electric car is €19,500 (approximately £17,160 or $27,930). In other words, a similar figure to what they would pay for any other family car.

It is significant that car manufacturers who already have experience of this electric car marketplace understand this and have developed new cars that are directly comparable in price to conventional cars. Manufacturers like GEM, BYD and REVA are already building a sustainable business model for themselves that do not rely on the whim of politicians and government handouts.

---

[56] Electric Vehicles: The Voice of the Consumer. Usage, Attitudes, Perception and Buying Interest in Electric Vehicles. Frost & Sullivan. October 2009.

Every mainstream manufacturer is currently dependent on government subsidies in order to achieve this comparison. While the political will exists to help fund the cars from these manufacturers, electric cars have the potential to establish themselves in the market. Yet if these mainstream manufacturers cannot reduce their production costs, they are creating an unsustainable future for themselves. They cannot rely on government subsidies for ever.

The future for electric cars may well be with a new generation of car makers. Manufacturers who can design and build cars from the ground up as electric vehicles, build them to the same quality standards as mainstream manufacturers do today and sell them at a price that competes directly with conventional cars.

APPENDIX B: ELECTRIC VEHICLES IN BUSINESS

Electric vehicles can make a lot of sense within a business environment. They provide economical transportation for inner city use and generate significant interest from both customers and the surrounding community, generating good publicity and goodwill.

However, they are not suitable for all businesses. Some businesses have had a lot of success using electric vehicles while others have experienced issues and found themselves running their businesses around the electric vehicles.

If you are planning to use an electric vehicle for business, you want to make sure they are going to be a success. For that reason, it is important to carefully evaluate whether or not an electric vehicle will suit your business needs.

Types of electric vehicle available

Electric Cars

Many businesses have one or more cars available for staff to visit customers. Estate agents, accountants, legal companies and insurance agents often have members of staff that need to be able to visit client sites, sometimes at a moment's notice.

Some businesses have found an electric car is ideally suited to this use. If you're based in a city and all your clients live in the same city, an electric car can be a quick way to get around.

Thanks to their ease of use, different members of staff can quickly get used to driving the car and electric cars have proven popular with employees and customers alike.

Electric minibuses and buses

Electric minibuses and buses are available. These range from 6 to 36 seater models. These are usually used for infrequent shuttle service rather than constant use and are usually used on large campuses, by hotels shuttling customers to and from airports or by retailers shuttling customers to and from their stores.

Commercial Vehicles

If you use vans, trucks or heavy goods vehicles for mainly city area and urban area work, there are now a number of electric vehicles available.

Most electric vans and trucks have a limited top speed, typically ranging from between 30mph (45km/h) and 50mph (80km/h), depending on the make and model. This limitation is rarely a problem in built up areas, where the high torque from the motor ensures the vehicles can keep up with other traffic on the roads but may be a limitation if using an electric vehicle outside of these areas.

Electric bicycles, motorbikes and scooters

If you use motorbikes for delivering small packages or take-away food to the surrounding area, an electric bicycle or electric motorbike may be a suitable option.

Insurance for pizza delivery motorbikes is expensive, whereas business insurance for an electric bike is very cheap. For distances of less than a mile at a time, an electric bike can be used to deliver goods just as quickly and effectively as a small motorbike.

So long as the overall distance travelled in a single shift is less than 10-15 miles (16-24km) and any one journey is less than one mile, an electric bike can be a very effective small delivery vehicle.

For longer distances, an electric motorbike can be an excellent alternative. Electric motorbikes have several advantages over more conventional motorbikes:

- Lower running costs.
- No engine noise that may disturb people in a residential area.
- Excellent stop-start performance.
- Some motorbikes, such as some of the excellent models in the Lexola range, include fast charging capabilities as standard, making a genuine 24/7 use vehicle.

Is an electric vehicle suitable for my business?

In order to answer that question, there are various steps you need to take to ensure that an electric vehicle is suitable.

Evaluate the types of journey

For business use, electric vehicles are best used in a city or urban environment. Long distance driving from one town to another is not so suitable for using an electric vehicle.

Electric commercial vehicles often have a limited top speed. This is fine for urban use but can be limiting for driving on freeways or across country.

The United Kingdom has a long history of electric commercial vehicle usage. The humble 'milk float' has been used from the 1920s to the present day for delivering milk and groceries to people's homes. This usage profile shows electric vehicles at their very best: lots of short journeys, frequent stops and a fixed route.

Electric commercial vehicles are exceptionally good in that particular environment, which is why they are particularly well suited to supermarket home deliveries, overnight parcel deliveries and postal applications.

Unless the overall range is limited, electric vehicles are not so useful for ad-hoc work where the distance driven can vary wildly from day to day. If you know the maximum distance the vehicle will have to travel is comfortably within the range of the vehicle, then this is not such an issue. However, look at the distance figures carefully to ensure this is the case.

Range

The biggest issue that businesses have with electric vehicles is range. All too often, a business will buy an electric vehicle in order to wave the green flag, only to find that their business requires them to travel further afield, or for more individual trips, than they anticipated.

The result is general frustration that the electric vehicle simply does not do what the business needs it to do. There is nothing more frustrating than having to turn down a customer because the electric vehicle is plugged in and needs to charge up.

Range fixation can also be an issue with employees using the electric vehicle. Drivers need to have the confidence that the vehicle will do what they need it to do.

It is vitally important that you spend time evaluating the distances that your current vehicles do every day. Once you know what range you need, look for an electric vehicle that is advertised as being able to do around double that range. This will cater for use in all conditions, with wipers, lights and heater or air conditioner running and driving with minimal consideration for fuel economy, or for handling unexpected diversions.

So if you require a vehicle that can travel 25 miles (40km) a day, look to buy one that can travel 50 miles (80km).

If you have the opportunity to recharge your vehicle throughout the day, such as during lunch breaks, you can take this into account when working out a suitable range.

Realistically, if you require a range of more than 70 miles a day without recharging, an electric vehicle is probably not the right vehicle for you at the moment. You would be better waiting for another two years before considering an electric vehicle for your business.

Access to charging points

If you are going to use an electric vehicle for business, you must ensure you are going to be able to charge it up when you need to.

In cities like London, where there is already a good public charging point network in place, you may be able to charge your vehicles at these points. However, you cannot rely on them as other people will also be using these points. Easily accessible off-road parking with charging facilities is almost always essential if using an electric vehicle for business.

Charging facilities and Commercial Vehicles

If you are contemplating a larger electric vehicle – such as a large van or a heavy goods vehicle, you are going to require a high voltage, high power electricity supply in order to charge the batteries.

In the UK, this means a 'three phase' 415v power supply, typically running at either 32 or 63 amps, while in the US a specific 'high voltage/high power' supply will need to be installed.

Electric Vehicles and employees

Just like a new electric car owner getting fixated on range on their new electric car, an employee driving a works-provided electric vehicle also gets fixated on range.

If an employee believes the electric vehicle is not going to have enough range to complete their journey (even if the vehicle does complete the journey but the 'fuel gauge' is low), it can undermine confidence in the vehicle, which can spread amongst other employees rapidly.

If there is an electric car charging point network in the town or city you are operating in, provide a satellite navigation system in the vehicle and program in all the charging point locations into the system. Even if the driver never uses the charging points, just knowing they are there gives them the confidence to use the vehicle and know they are not going to be left stranded without power.

Promoting your business with Electric Vehicles

Eye catching electric vehicles such as the Aixam Mega or Modec electric vans, or the G-Wiz, NMG or Aptera electric vehicles make excellent promotional vehicles for a business.

In fact all electric vehicles are attention grabbing and generate positive interest.

If they are sign written, they can generate business enquiries for your business and there are few better ways of increase your reputation as an environmentally friendly business.

If you are looking to use an electric vehicle as part of your business and want to ensure it also promotes your business, make sure it is well sign written.

If your business is operating in an area where there are very few electric vehicles in use, make sure you also contact the trade press and the local newspapers and radio stations as well. Local journalists are always looking for an interesting news angle and you'll often get a lot of free publicity as a result.

Public charging points

If your business is installing an outside power socket in order to charge up an electric vehicle, why not install two power sockets and make one available to other electric car owners?

If you run a shop or a restaurant, you'll be encouraging electric car owners to use your business and if not you can use the fact you're installing an extra electric car charging point as a great publicity tool to help promote your business.

Electric Commercial Vehicles you can buy today

Small vans and light trucks

Make	Model	Notes
Allied Electric	Peugeot eExpert	A Peugeot Expert converted to electric power. Available in the UK and Ireland.
Aixam Mega	MultiTruck	Available across Europe as a small van, drop side, pickup, tipper or chassis cab.
Citroen	Berlingo Electrique	Compact van produced from 1999 to 2006. Available used across Europe.
Ford	Transit Connect	Compact van becoming available in 2010 in North America only.
Goupil	G3	A small utility truck popular with local government.

Make	Model	Notes
GEM	eS eL eL-XD	Available in the United States and across Europe as a box van or pickup.
Miles	ZX40ST	A useful size work truck available across the United States.
Piaggio	Ape Electric Porter Electric	The Ape is a tiny three wheel micro-van popular in Asia; the Porter is a small van, truck and a six seat mini-bus. Sold in Europe.
Renault	Kangoo Z.E.	An electric version of the new Renault Kangoo. First vehicles available in 2011.
Stevens	ZeVan	A small electric van built in the United Kingdom.

Large Vans

Make	Model	Notes
Allied Electric	Peugeot eBoxer	A Peugeot Boxer converted to electric power. Available in the UK and Ireland.
BBIG	QEV	Becoming available in 2010 in the UK as a van, truck or chassis cab. Unique hot-swap battery system.
Modec	Modec	Available across Europe, starting to become available in North America as a box van, truck or chassis cab.
Smiths	Edison	An electric version of the Ford Transit. Available in Europe only as a van, truck, chassis cab or minibus.

Heavy Goods Vehicles

Make	Model	Notes
Smiths	Newton	Available across Europe, starting to become available in North America. 7.5 ton to 12 ton models.

Electric Bikes, Motor Scooters and Motorbikes

Make	Model	Notes
Brammo	Enertia	Electric motorbike
Lexola	Various electric motor scooters	Available worldwide
Urban Mover	Various electric bikes	Available worldwide
Vectrix	Electric motor scooter	Available worldwide
Zero	DS MX X	Range of electric motorbikes available in North America and Europe.

Buses and Coaches

Make	Model	Notes
Astonbus	E-City	A range of city buses and coaches in electric and hybrid variants.
Optare	Solo EV	A midi bus capable of carrying up to 37 passengers, available in Europe.
Proterra	Transit Bus	A 35 foot long electric transit bus currently in trial in the United States.

Chapter Summary

- Electric vehicles can make a lot of sense within a business environment.

- They provide economical transportation for inner city use.

- They generate significant interest from both customers and the surrounding community, generating good publicity and goodwill.

- Ensuring an electric vehicle is a good 'fit' for your business requires careful evaluation of the way you use your existing vehicles.

- Electric vehicles can be a very effective way of promoting your business.

- There is a reasonable selection of electric commercial vehicles available on the market today.

APPENDIX C: ELECTRIC VEHICLES AND LOCAL GOVERNMENT

Governments, councils and public bodies are under pressure to reduce their carbon footprint. Implementing electric vehicles is a very positive way of demonstrating this.

As well as reducing the carbon footprint, electric vehicles are extremely visible to members of the public. They give the public a very clear sign of leadership that the government is making a stand.

Electric vehicles can very easily be used in many areas of local government and within public bodies. Park maintenance, city centre maintenance, shuttle bus services, internal mail delivery and community support are just a few of the ways that electric vehicles have been successfully implemented by public bodies.

How local government can help the adoption of electric vehicles in their locality

There are lots of ways that local government can help the adoption of electric vehicles in their locality.

Many of these can be carried out at little or no expense and in many countries there are central government subsidies available to assist in the more expensive tasks.

Free Parking

Offering free or reduced cost parking to electric car users is a simple way to encourage electric car ownership.

Allowing electric cars to use multi-occupancy lanes

Where cities have lanes dedicated for cars with at least one passenger, opening these lanes to owners of electric cars is another simple way to encourage electric car ownership.

Some councils have gone further and allowed electric cars access to bus lanes. While this may encourage early adoption of electric vehicles, it is likely to cause problems later. On balance, this is probably not to be recommended.

Electric car charging points

Providing public charging points is the single biggest thing that a council can do to encourage electric car usage. Depending on how it is achieved, it can either be done on a strict budget or at great expense.

If a council is planning to implement their own electric vehicles, they are going to need to install charging points for these vehicles.

These charging points are typically an outside power socket, fitted to a wall. If councils are installing these, they should consider installing them in publically accessible areas and allow other electric car owners access to these charging points.

Installing power supplies in multi-storey car parks, where the power already exists, is a relatively straightforward and cheap way to provide public charging points. The spaces must be reserved for electric car owners who are charging their vehicles and this must be enforced.

If cost is a concern, councils can charge electric car users for electricity use through an additional tariff on the car park ticket. Many car park ticket machines already have the ability to add ad-hoc tariffs in this way.

Many councils have expressed concerns that these charging points may be damaged or deliberately abused. Although this is a valid concern, London councils who have already installed charging points say they have not experienced these problems.

On street charging points is another option but are significantly more expensive to install. Companies like Elektromotive, Pod Point and Park and Power in the United Kingdom and GreenlightAC in the United States all supply and install on street electric car charging posts.

Incidentally, for electric car charging points to become viable, they must be available to all electric car owners and not just those who live in the area the charging points are being installed in. In the past, some councils have installed charging points but have then barred any electric car owners except those living in the region from using them.

This is a pointless exercise that causes a lot of frustration and loss of goodwill amongst electric vehicle owners: local owners are able to charge from home and don't need charging points within a mile or two of their house, while other electric car owners are unable to use the facilities and therefore are less likely to travel to that area.

Encouraging local businesses

'At Work' and 'Gone Shopping' charging points are also highly beneficial for some electric car owners and will help encourage electric car ownership. Encouraging local businesses to offer these can benefit their own businesses as well as their employees and the community at large.

When private enterprises are submitting plans for retail parks or industrial areas, request that electric car charging points are incorporated into the design.

Charging at Home

Many people who would like to be able to own an electric car do not have off-road parking available to them. Offering a paid for service to install a power bollard and reserve a space outside the owner's home, at their own expense, will encourage a number of people who currently have nowhere to charge up an electric car to buy them.

Do people use electric cars instead of bus services?

One concern that many councils have is that encouraging electric cars will take people off the buses and back into their own cars again.

The G-Wiz Electric Car Owners Club ran a poll amongst its London-based members in 2007, asking the membership if they bought an electric car instead of using public transport. Every single member who responded to the survey said this was not the case.

Other than this arbitrary questionnaire, very little research has been carried out into this. The City of London used this concern as a reason to remove free parking for electric cars from their car parks, yet admitted at the time they had carried out no definitive research into this.

At present, the best that can be said is that it appears unlikely that people buy electric cars as an alternative to using public transport.

Chapter Summary

- Electric vehicles can work well in a number of applications within local government and public bodies.

- If you are installing charging points for your own electric vehicles, why not install some of them in publically available locations and offer them to other electric car users.

- Local government has a part to play in encouraging electric car ownership amongst the community. Start with the simple, low cost options and build from there.

- Encouraging local businesses to play their part is also important.

- Offer charging options for people who have no off-road parking. You won't be able to help everyone but you will be able to help some.

- There is no evidence to suggest that people use electric cars instead of public transport.

APPENDIX D: OTHER ELECTRIC VEHICLES

Electric vehicles are not just limited to electric cars. Electric bikes, motorbikes and commercial vehicles have been available for a number of years.

Some of these vehicles have become very successful. Electric bikes, for instance, have become a worldwide phenomenon with over 100 million now in use around the world.

Electric Bicycles

Twenty one million electric bicycles were sold during 2008 in China alone and worldwide over one hundred million people use an electric bicycle on a regular basis.

Without doubt the most popular electric vehicle around, an electric bicycle is simply a pedal cycle with electrical assistance. In Europe and the United States, they are regarded in law as pedal cycles and can be used by anyone aged 14 or over without road tax or insurance.

In the UK, electric bicycles have gained popularity with commuters and with older people who still want the freedom of a bicycle without the hard work cycling up the hills.

Top speed is typically 15mph (25km/h) and the range is usually around 15–25 miles (25-40km). The batteries can usually be detached from the bike and taken inside for charging and some customers choose to buy two battery packs so they always have one charged up and ready to go.

A budget electric bicycle can be bought from around £200 in the UK, or $300 in the US, with quality makes start from around £600 in the UK and $900 in the US. Urban Mover is one of the leading manufacturers of electric bikes.

Electric Motorbikes and Scooters

Electric motorbikes and scooters are also gaining in popularity, predominantly as commuter vehicles.

If you have only driven a car in the past, you may need to take another test before being allowed to drive a motorcycle. Legislation varies depending on the power of the motorcycle, when you took your original driving test and which country you live in.

Most electric motorbikes are scooter styled bikes, with a range of 40–50 miles (65–80km). Top speed varies depending on the power required but are typically between 30mph (45km/h) and 65mph (105km/h).

Prices for electric motorbikes are comparable to the equivalent combustion engine motorbikes. Zero and Brammo are the two leading manufacturers of electric motorbikes and Lexola and Vectrix are the two leading manufacturers of electric scooters. Peugeot are also planning an electric scooter at the end of 2010.

Electric Commercial Vehicles

There is a separate appendix on electric vehicles in business that covers this area in more detail but a number of electric commercial vehicles are already available on the market.

The two main players in the market are Modec and Smiths. Both of these are English companies and have sales operations in North America.

Smiths have been working with Ford on the Ford Transit Connect EV, being launched in North America in 2010.

Most electric vans have a range of around 100 miles (160km). At present, they are expensive to buy. However, much of this additional cost is offset by the significantly lower running cost of the vehicles, especially if spread over a five year ownership.

Electric Aircraft

It is unlikely that you will be boarding an electric aircraft for an international flight any time soon but amongst small, lightweight private aircraft such as micro lights and powered gliders, electric variants are now available.

Flight time is currently limited to around one hour and speeds are low. At present, electric aircraft are really enthusiast's toys for recreational use only but perhaps in the future, a practical electric aircraft could become a reality.

NASA has built an experimental remotely controlled solar powered electric aircraft that has flown for 17 hours non-stop.

Electric Boats

Small electric boats for inland waterways have become popular as recreational craft over the past ten years.

They are popular because they are silent and because they are cheap to buy and run. You can buy an electric powered outboard motor and battery for around half the price of an equivalent combustion engine outboard with fuel tank.

As electric boats are silent, they do not disturb wildlife, making exploring rivers and lakes particularly enjoyable.

The motors do not need to be excessively big or powerful, so even a modest sized leisure battery, as used in caravans and RVs, can provide eight hours or more of power. Many people have combined their electric boat with a solar panel so the boat can recharge when it is not in use.

Chapter Summary

- Electric vehicles have quietly been making inroads into the market for the past ten years.

- Even if an electric car is not a practical solution for you now, there are other electric powered vehicles available that are suitable for recreational or utility use.

APPENDIX E: FREE – WORKING TOWARDS A RADICAL PRICE

I am often asked whether electricity will become the dominant fuel for cars in the next few years. I believe it will but the timescale for this switch is unclear. Much of it will depend on the cars that become available and how quickly consumers see the benefits and advantages of electric cars.

Many industry commentators believe that by 2020, only two or three percent of the cars on our roads will be electric. Renault and Nissan believe the take-up will be much faster, with 10% of all new cars being electric powered by 2020.

Undoubtedly there will be a few incidents along the way and just as undoubtedly, some cars will be better than others. Yet I personally believe that at some point, electricity will become the dominant fuel for cars and that the take up could be much quicker than currently anticipated.

My reasoning is one of simple economics. In the long term, oil prices are only ever going to go up higher and higher. Meanwhile, the price of an electric car is going to fall. Eventually, the cost of leasing an electric car will be cheaper than the cost of putting fuel into a conventional car.

At that point, the cost of the electric car itself is effectively zero.

Anyone want a free car?

Throughout the world, top economists have been talking about how business and buying patterns will evolve over the next thirty years.

There is consensus amongst these economists that the real cost of many products and services will drop significantly, to the point where many of the products and services we currently pay for become free.

In his recent book, *Free: the Future of a Radical Price*, Chris Anderson argues that the economics of abundance forces the devaluation of products and services to the point where they are virtually free. Zero pricing is changing the face of business. Chris argues that businesses and industries have the choice of either adopting this strategy for themselves or becoming victims of it.

For a product to be free there has to be another product or service that can be charged for. The free product must also be low maintenance with negligible ongoing costs associated with it.

The mobile phone model

A good example of a free product that we all have and use are cell phones. If you walk into a cell phone shop, almost all the phones are offered free of charge. You simply choose the model, choose your usage tariff and off you go. If you are an existing customer with an older phone, you can upgrade your phone and still not pay anything for your new purchase.

The actual manufacturing cost of the phones is most certainly not free. Many phones actually cost many hundreds for the phone companies to buy. The profits made on monthly usage charges are used to write off the cost of the phone itself.

Making the mobile phone sales model work for cars

By removing the dependence on oil, this sales model will be able to work for electric cars in the future. The cars themselves will be free and customers choose a usage tariff that suits them.

Usage tariffs will directly replace the fuel bills that everyone has to pay to use their existing cars and will be calculated to work out either the same cost or slightly cheaper than the cost for putting fuel into an equivalent combustion engine car.

So instead of paying £250 or $250 per month for fuel at service stations, you would pay a similar amount each month for the usage plan on your electric car. The electric car itself would be free. At the start of your contract you'd be able to go into the car showroom, choose the car that you want and simply drive it away.

Given the choice between buying a $15,000 car with a combustion engine and then paying $250 per month on fuel, or just paying the $250 a month on a usage plan and getting the equivalent electric car for free, which would you choose?

Of course, none of this is going to happen overnight. It took the mobile phone industry around fifteen years to get to the point where phones were given away free of charge and it will certainly take a number of years for the car industry to get to the same position.

Expect it to happen. Walking into your local car dealership will be like walking into your local mobile phone store.

Of course, this model could only work with electric cars. With hydrogen cars or petrol/gasoline or diesel cars, you still have to pay for fuel so there is no cost saving available to customers. For that reason and that reason alone, electric cars will become the dominant type of vehicle on our roads.

Why would anyone choose anything different?

APPENDIX F: CHARGING AN ELECTRIC CAR WITH RENEWABLE POWER

Many people who buy an electric car want to reduce their impact on the environment. So it is probably not a surprise that many of them decide they want to charge their cars up using a renewable energy source, such as solar or wind power.

Charging up an electric car with solar

If you want to charge up an electric car with solar power, it helps if you live in a sunny climate with a good amount of sun throughout the year. If you live in California or Italy for example, it is possible to use sun power to charge and run your electric car all year round.

Elsewhere, in Northern Europe or Canada for example, you are unlikely to be able to generate enough power in the winter months to make your car fully solar powered.

The easiest solution for charging up an electric car with solar power is to build a grid-tied solar array. This generates electricity that can then be used to charge up the car, run the family home or be sold back to the utility companies if the array is generating electricity when you don't need it.

Costs for installing solar power are falling but don't expect a solar charging system to be cheap. Even in sunny climates you are likely to require a 1kWh solar array at least in order to charge up an electric car on a daily basis, at a likely cost of £3,000-£5,000 in the UK, or $5,000–$8000 in the United States.

Of course, if you need a shorter daily range, you can use a smaller solar array. A company called Alpha Energy in Phoenix, Arizona, has recently launched a new scalable solar electric charger called the EV-500. This unit is specifically designed for charging up 48v electric vehicles, such as many smaller electric city cars, NEVs and electric scooters.

Solar powered cars

Three electric car makers have announced solar powered cars. Venturi and REVA are all planning to have solar powered cars for sale in the near future. SunMotor have gone one better and are already shipping solar powered cars to customers.

Figure 9- The Venturi Eclectic solar car

The first two cars on the road will be the SunMotor DX and the Venturi Eclectic, with the REVA NXR with optional solar panel roof arriving a few months later.

All three cars are compact, road legal electric cars with solar panels mounted on the roof.

The Venturi Eclectic and SunMotor DX are designed for city and urban driving with frequent stops and low speed driving whereas the REVA NXR, a more practical four seat car, is capable of longer and faster trips.

The solar panels on the Venturi Eclectic are designed to provide a top up charge rather than provide the sole power source. Purely on solar power and in a sunny climate, sunlight can provide a solar-powered range of around 5 miles (8 km) a day. An optional clip-on wind turbine adds a further 8 miles (13 km).

The SunMotor DX and REVA NXR go a step further. The cars have larger solar panels on the roof, providing a range of up to 15 miles (24km) a day purely on sun power.

With all the cars, the range can be extended by plugging the car into a standard power socket.

Although the range may not seem that great, there are many drivers who live in a sunny climate and only use their cars for short journeys a few times each week. For these people, they could now drive an entirely solar powered car.

These cars are not going to be suitable for everyone. Yet the first exciting steps towards practical solar road cars have been made. With the advancement of solar panels with better capacities and lower costs and the ongoing development of electric cars, it may not be that long before solar electric cars become a common sight on our roads.

Commercially Available Solar Charging Stations

The first commercially available solar charging stations are now appearing.

Beautiful Earth, a New York based sustainable energy company, has unveiled its first solar charging station in Brooklyn. Powered purely on sunlight and with no mains grid connection, the system is built using recycled shipping containers and can charge up an electric car faster than plugging one into a standard power socket.

Meanwhile, in the United Kingdom, the Cross Group has recently unveiled a commercial multi-bay solar powered electric vehicle charger. Designed for businesses and local government, the system allows multiple charging points to be installed anywhere, without requiring a mains power connection.

At a cost of around £30,000 (approximately $48,000), it is comparable in price to installing multiple street level charging points on a busy street.

The technology, the products and potential to have a solar powered electric car charging network covering an entire country does now exist. Surely, it can only now be a matter of time before a country implements one?

Finding out more about solar

If you are interested in finding out more about solar power, I would recommend visiting www.SolarElectricityHandbook.com to find out more about the technology. The website includes a solar project analysis tool that allows you to estimate the size and cost of a suitable solar implementation.

Wind Power

Wind turbines are gaining popularity, both as a way of generating large amounts of power for the utility grid and also as a way of generating small scale energy for a household.

Wind power is nothing new. Back in the 1920s and 1930s, wind turbines were used by many farms in order to provide electricity. Their use died out as the utility grids expanded, providing cheap, dependable electricity at the flick of a switch.

Today, large scale wind turbines are efficient and effective. They can be installed in a variety of locations comparatively quickly. Unlike the early large wind turbines, modern turbines are virtually silent and the largest systems can generate between two and six megawatts of power.

Small wind turbines do have disadvantages however and are very site specific. Compared to large wind turbines used by the power companies, small wind turbines are not particularly efficient and need to be situated in an area of above average wind in order to generate reasonable amounts of power.

Wind turbines also require a very smooth airflow. Smaller turbines are very susceptible to turbulence. If you live near to a busy road, or near trees, or in a built up area, a wind turbine is unlikely to work well for you. Turbulent air (where the wind is constantly changing direction) leaves the wind turbines constantly chasing the wind direction rather than extracting power from it.

If you have the right location, wind power can work extremely effectively. Wind turbines work best in open exposed areas where average wind speeds are high.

Ideally, wind turbines should be mounted high up. Even small wind turbines are often mounted 8-10 meters high in order to get sufficient wind power. Turbines should also be installed away from buildings. Roof mounting a wind turbine is not ideal as the building itself generates turbulence and the vibrations from a wind turbine being affected by turbulent air can be magnified through brick walls, creating a loud and annoying vibrating sound.

Small wind turbines can often be found on small leisure boats. The turbine maintains the batteries when the boats are not in use. Boat owners have mixed reports on their benefits:

- Owners who have the turbines mounted relatively low down on the boat find they do not perform well at all.

- Owners who have the turbines mounted high up on a mast report much better performance from their wind turbines.

Fitting a wind turbine onto an electric car

I have been asked on a number of occasions whether it would be beneficial to fit a wind turbine onto an electric car.

Fitting a turbine to a car and using it while driving the car would not work. The amount of additional drag created by the wind resistance would outweigh the benefit of the electricity generation from the turbine.

Fitting a turbine to a parked car in order to recharge the batteries is a possibility but is unlikely to yield significant results. Electric cars are typically used in built up areas with poor wind flow so unless the car is parked in an open, windy location, the amount of power generated by the turbines is likely to be very small.

Chapter Summary

- Many people buy an electric car in order to reduce their impact on the environment. These people can reduce their impact further by using renewable power.

- If you have solar panels on your home, you can use solar energy to charge up your electric car during the daytime. This is more feasible in sunny climates, such as the southern states of America than it is in Canada or Northern Europe.

- You can buy a solar charger kit specifically designed to charge up an electric car. Again, this is more feasible in sunnier climates than others.

- Cars with solar panels mounted on the roof are becoming available. In the right climate, short distance drivers could find that a solar car could provide all the power they ever need.

- The technology and products required to build a nationwide network of electric car solar charging stations already exists.

- A wind turbine could be used to generate electricity for charging an electric car but a turbine that is mounted to the car when it is parked is likely to be very inefficient and not produce enough power.

APPENDIX H: THE WEBSITE

Accompanying this book is a new website containing up to date news and information about electric cars and lots more besides. You can find the site at:

www.OwningElectricCar.com

The site is dynamic and constantly being improved with new information and functionality being added all the time.

Here is a preview of what you will find on the site:

Electric Car Articles

There are a number of articles about the latest technology and information about electric cars and electric car ownership, written by world class authors and writers who are specialists in the electric car industry.

Energy Calculators

Want to know the best time to plug in your electric car? With our online energy monitor, you can see where your electricity is coming from and the current carbon footprint for each kilowatt-hour of electricity based on the current energy mix.

Podcasts and Videos

Podcasts and videos about electric cars and various aspects of electric car ownership.

Website Directory

A directory of websites about electric cars and electric car ownership from all around the web.

Ask me a question

Have a question about electric cars? Have a comment about the book, or a suggestion on how it can be improved? Drop me a line via the website.

Frequently Asked Questions

A constantly updated list of questions and answers, based on the questions sent to me. Look through the questions asked by other people and read the responses.

Want More?

If you feel there is something I have missed out in the book, or should include on the web site, get in touch with me and tell me. Visit the web site and follow the 'ask me a question' link.

I can't promise that I'll be able to provide what you are after, but I can promise you that I will consider it.

GLOSSARY

BEV	Battery Electric Vehicle. An electric vehicle using batteries for energy storage.
EAPC	Electrically Assisted Pedal Cycle – the correct term for road legal electric bicycles in Europe. EAPCs can be ridden on the road by anyone aged 14 or over without road tax, insurance or safety helmet.
EV	Electric Vehicle. A vehicle using an electric motor instead of a combustion engine.
Fuel Cell	A fuel cell is a power generator that produces electricity through chemical reaction with fuel – typically hydrogen – as opposed to burning the fuel, as with a combustion engine.
	Fuel cells typically extract twice as much power from their fuel source than combustion engines but run at a much slower rate.
HEV	Hybrid Electric Vehicle – a hybrid system using an electric motor and a combustion engine.
KERS	**Kinetic Energy Recovery System** – *see Regenerative Braking.*
LiFePO4	Lithium-ion battery chemistry made from a combination of lithium (Li), Iron (Fe) and Phosphate (PO4), typically used in electric vehicles.
Lithium-Ion	Lithium-Ion is currently the battery technology of choice for high end electric cars. The chemical structure of the battery is different from the lithium-ion batteries found in laptop computers and mobile phones, designed for heavy duty use and a longer life.
Long Tail Pipe	A phrase used to describe the pollution of an electric car at the power station generating the electricity.
PHEV	Plug-in Hybrid Electric Vehicle – a hybrid car that can have its batteries charged by plugging into a power socket and not just by running the engine.
REEV	Range Extended Electric Vehicle – *see Plug-in Hybrid Electric Vehicle.*

185

Regenerative Braking	Using the electric motor to slow down the car, storing the energy generated from the momentum of the car in the batteries.
	When driving around town, about 30% of the energy used to power an electric vehicle is recaptured during braking.
	Regenerative braking is also known as KERS.
PACTS	Parliamentary Advisory Council for Transport Safety. A group in the United Kingdom that advises the British government on transport safety.
Project Better Place	A multi-national company working with governments and car manufacturers, installing electric car charging points, battery swap-out stations and building an economic model for the rapid acceptance of electric cars.
Smart Metering	Electricity metering that shows the home-owner what electricity is being used at any time, along with the cost of that electricity, so that the home owner can make informed decisions as to what power they should be using at any one time.
	Some smart metering systems can work with 'smart appliances' such as washing machines and electric cars, in order to switch on automatically when electricity is cheap and switch off when electricity is expensive.
Tailpipe Emissions	Refers to the pollution created from the exhaust pipe on a car. Electric cars have no 'tailpipe emissions' because the pollution is produced where the electricity is generated rather than where it is used.
Traction batteries	Heavy duty lead acid batteries used for electric vehicles.
Ultra capacitors	Ultra capacitors are a potential future alternative for batteries in electric vehicles.
	Already in use in some hybrids, ultra capacitors have a claimed lifespan of one million recharges.
Vehicle-to-Grid	Vehicle-to-Grid technology is a concept for using an electric vehicles battery as an energy store for the utility grid: the car charging up using cheap, overnight electricity and selling it back during peak demand at a profit, should the car not be needed.
Wet Batteries	Lead acid batteries that require watering on a regular basis.

INDEX

Aerodynamics

    Wind Resistance 27, 181

Air Pollution105, 106, 111, 112, 122, 124

    Asthma........................ 111, 112

    Power Station....................... 112

Aixam7, 55, 60, 93, 133, 134, 139, 162, 163

    Mega City . 55, 60, 133, 134, 139

    MultiTruck 163

American Electric Vehicle........... 61

Aptera 56, 61, 162

ARUP 92

Asthma................. See Air Pollution

Batteries

    Distilled Water...................... 97

    Environmental Impact... 104, 136

    Guarantees 32

    Lead Acid32, 89, 91, 136, 137, 186

    Leasing.................................. 47

    LiFePO4.............................. 185

    Lithium ion . 32, 91, 96, 138, 185

    Nickel Metal Hydride 32, 136

Battery

    Replacement32, 47, 48, 49, 94, 141

Battery Vehicle Society50, 89, 94, 100

BBIG... 164

Better Place 13, 186

BMW............................. 17, 34, 150

Braking...................... 22, 185, 186

Buddy ....See Kewet

BYD 62, 142

Car Club 13, 36, 42

    Chicago................................. 36

    City Car Club........................ 36

    Zipcar.....................................

Car hire..................................... 42

Car Sharing............................... 43

Carbon Footprint35, 104, 119, 123, 130, 131, 134, 137, 138, 139, 140, 141, 145, 146, 167, 183

    Dust to Dust......................... 140

Charging at work................... 29, 41

Charging Point

    Shops 12

Charging Points11, 12, 29, 30, 31, 41, 150, 161, 162, 179, 186

    At Home 39, 169

    Caravan Sites......................... 28

    Dynamic Charging................. 92

    Elektromotive 168

    EV Network..................... 30, 50

    GreenlightAC 168

    Hotel 28

    Independent Businesses29, 40, 163, 169

Nationwide Charging Infrastructure3, 4, 13, 31, 92, 129

Park and Power 168

Pod Point................................ 168

Power Bollard 40, 169

Pubs...28

Restaurants..............................28

Shops................................29, 169

Static IPT 92

Chevrolet 17, 34, 135

Chrysler 52, 68, 75, 153

Citroen 62, 63, 66, 93, 100, 163

Berlingo 62, 163

Coal.................. 113, 119, 120, 121

Coda..64

Combustion engine8, 9, 15, 17, 18, 19, 27, 45, 47, 48, 72, 75, 79, 104, 128, 131, 135, 142, 152, 172, 173, 175, 185

CommuterCars............................64

Crude oil 115, 116

Diesel Particulate Matter 108

Drax Power Station.................... 122

Duo 56, 74

Dynamic ChargingSee Charging Points

Dynasty................................. 65, 93

Effedi 65

Electric Aircraft 172, 173

Electric Auto Association 94, 100

Electric Bicycle.......... 159, 171, 185

Electric Boat 173

Electric Bus................. 92, 140, 159

Astonbus 165

Optare 165

Proterra 165

Electric minibus......................... 159

Electric Motorbike............. 159, 172

Electric Truck............................ 159

Electric Van.............. 159, 162, 172

Elektromotive ...See Charging Points

El-Jet ....70, See Kewet

Emissions17, 18, 20, 104, 105, 107, 108, 109, 110, 111, 112, 113, 114, 118, 120, 122, 123, 124, 125, 130, 131, 133, 135, 138, 142

Biodiesel....................... 109, 110

Carbon Monoxide107, 108, 109, 110, 111, 121

Diesel............................. 19, 107

Electricity Production 113

Nitrogen Oxide107, 109, 111, 121, 122, 123

Sulphur Dioxide.... 111, 121, 122

Tank to Wheel104, 110, 135, 145, 147

Well to Wheel104, 114, 118, 131, 135, 147

Emissions Trading Scheme 142

Environment18, 22, 27, 37, 103, 139, 142, 152, 153, 158, 160, 166, 177, 181

environmental....... See Environment

Estrima 66

EV Network .....See Charging Points

EV-Cast....................................... 5

Fast Charging8, 11, 12, 30, 35, 80, 130

Fiat 35, 93, 153

Ford35, 67, 84, 85, 93, 100, 135, 152, 153, 163, 164, 172

Ranger 49, 67

Tourneo 67

Transit Connect....... 67, 163, 172

Free Car 174

Fuel Cell 4, 15, 16, 19, 185

Fuel Economy37, 105, 108, 131, 143, 161, *See* Range

Gas fired power station.............. 123

GEM7, 52, 68, 75, 93, 139, 153, 164

General Motors 34, 35, 93, 153, 156

    EV1 .... 153, 154

Geo-thermal energy 113, 124

Goupil 163

Green Eco Mobility ....*See* GEM

Green Vehicles 69

GreenlightAC... *See* Charging Points

G-Wiz .... 139, *See* Reva G-Wiz

Honda15, 16, 17, 18, 34, 93, 135, 139, 150, 153, 156

    FCX Clairty............................. 16

Hybrid4, 12, 15, 17, 18, 19, 86, 129, 185

Hydro-electricity........................ 125

Hydrogen ....*See* Fuel Cell

Hydrogen Fuel Stations 16

Induction Power Transfer 92

Kandi 69

Kewet... 69

    Buddy..................................... 70

    El Jet 70

    MetroBuddy 70

Leasing 45

LEED.. 140

Liberty 71

Low Speed Vehicles 54

LSV...........*See* Low Speed Vehicles

Maranello 4Cycle .... *See* Effedi

Medium Speed Vehicle 53

Mercedes 49, 80, 141

METRObuddy.................*See* Kewet

Miles Automotive....................... 71

Milk Float................................. 160

MINI.............36, 45, 46, 71, 72, 135

Mitsubishi7, 10, 20, 38, 45, 46, 72, 73, 76, 95, 133, 134, 136, 144, 155

    i-MiEV10, 20, 38, 46, 72, 73, 76, 133, 134, 144, 146, 155

Mobile Phone 13, 35, 36, 176

Modec.................... 162, 164, 172

MyCar 73

National Grid............. 113, 128, 130

Neighborhood Electric Vehicle .. 26, 53

    NEV26, 49, 52, 54, 61, 69, 82, 85, 87, 88

NEV*See* Neighborhood Electric Vehicle

Nuclear Power.................. 119, 124

Oil power station 123

Owners Clubs 94, 95, 101

PACTS 14, 186

Park and Power.*See* Charging Points

Performance4, 21, 22, 25, 26, 52, 56, 61, 64, 71, 72, 75, 79, 80, 83, 84, 88, 89, 94, 96, 98, 99, 105, 118, 122, 131, 181

Peugeot.............34, 76, 93, 100, 150

Phoenix............................. 76, 177

Piaggio............................... 93, 164

Pod Point ....*See* Charging Points

Pollution

    Diesel............................. 19, 109

Pumped Storage........................ 126

189

Purchasing45, 47, 48, 49, 51, 62, 95, 175

Quadricycle........ 51, 54, 55, 60, 155

Range9, 10, 11, 12, 13, 15, 16, 18, 19, 22, 23, 24, 25, 26, 27, 28, 30, 31, 32, 33, 35, 36, 38, 39, 41, 44, 56, 60, 61, 67, 71, 72, 74, 80, 82, 84, 87, 89, 90, 92, 94, 95, 96, 98, 107, 133, 134, 160, 161, 162, 171, 172, 177, 178, 179

Range Fixation.......................23, 24

Recycling105, 122, 137, 140, 141, 179

Regenerative Braking18, 22, 23, 27, 96, 99

Renault..... 13, 77, 93, 154, 156, 174

Clio Electro 78

Resale Values 48, 49

Reva34, 35, 46, 51, 68, 79, 80, 93, 95, 133, 134, 139, 140, 144, 178, 179

G-Wiz5, 34, 48, 49, 50, 68, 79, 80, 133, 134, 144, 150, 154, 156, 162, 169

NXG..35

NXR...... 35, 51, 79, 80, 178, 179

Reva Electric Car Club 95

Road Noise 14, 21

Running Costs.......... 33, 37, 46, 150

Servicing....................... 48, 49, 100

Silence 13, 14, 15, 21, 173, 180

Smart.. 45, 73, 80, 81, 135, 150, 186

Smart Meter 130

Smiths 67, 164, 165, 172

Solar5, 35, 82, 87, 89, 90, 127, 128, 140, 173, 177, 178, 179, 180, 181, 182

Start Lab 61, 81

Stevens 82, 164

ZeCar 82

SunMotor.................... 82, 178, 179

Tango ....*See* CommuterCars

Tata.. 83

Indica Vista............................ 83

Tazzari...................................... 83

Zero 83, 84

Tesla 10, 84, 95, 155

TH!NK 67, 84, 85, 153

City 85

Neighbor................................. 85

Three Wheeled Vehicles*See* Tricycle

Toxic Organic Micro Pollutants 107

Toyota 17, 86, 93, 100, 135, 136

RAV4.................................... 86

Triac 56, 69

Tricycle 51, 55, 56

Twike 86

Ultra Capacitors........................ 186

Venturi................................ 87, 178

Eclectic 87, 178

Fetish 87

Website.........95, 130, 134, 149, 183

Wheego 87

Wind Noise........................... 14, 21

Wind Turbine 126, 127, 180, 181

ZAP 88, 93

Xebra 88

Zipcar .... *See* Car Club

Also by Michael Boxwell:

The Solar Electricity Handbook

2010 Edition

Solar electricity is a wonderful concept - take free power from the sun and use it to power electrical equipment. No ongoing electricity bills, no reliance on an electrical socket - 'free' energy that doesn't harm the planet.

Of course, the reality is a little different from that. Yet generating electricity from sunlight alone is a powerful resource with applications and benefits throughout the world.

But how does it work? What is it suitable for? How much does it cost? How do I install it? This internet-linked solar book answers all these questions and shows you how you can use the power of the sun to generate electricity yourself.

For 2010, this book has been extensively updated - with new chapters, new diagrams and updated information, ensuring it offers completely up-to-date information about solar technology.

The web site that accompanies this book includes online solar calculators and tools to simplify your solar electricity installation; ensuring building your solar electric systems is as straightforward and successful as possible.

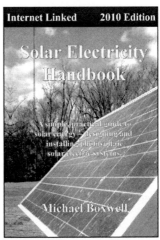

Now is the time to get on board with this exciting technology. Whether you simply want to learn the basics of how solar electricity works or if you are planning to install your own solar electric system, then this handbook will provide you with everything you need to know.

www.SolarElectricityHandbook.com

The Trousers
of Reality

by Barry Evans

Find your balance in life, work and play

This book explores the knowledge and wisdom of 3000 years. It shows how the discoveries of the great philosophers and scientists are about what you do every day. It proposes that there is a root and branch to excellence and that skills distilled in one context can be transferred to another.

As a case study it focuses on the transfer of skills between programming software and Management. It shows that the deep principles that make both work are reciprocal.

Art, philosophy, psychology, history, science, music and DIY are explored in a search for principles that work. It shows you how to discover why they work and how to apply all of the skills you might have however you came by them.

This book is for you if you would like to understand how to make best use of all of the resources available to you. It is aimed at those who see life, both work and play, as an amazing opportunity to achieve excellence and find meaning in every breath. This book will not teach you to think outside the box. It will make you question the existence of boxes.

www.TrousersOfReality.com

Here's to a fun, Green future.

Now that you've had a chance to read up on electric cars, how about finding out more?

littleCollie produces podcasts, online content and applications to help you reduce the impact that your life has on the planet, without impacting your enjoyment of it. Here's just two of the shows we help make. We think you'll like them!

Our weekly flagship show - ThisWeekinEnergy, is hosted by Nikki Gordon-Bloomfield and Bob Tregilus. Each week they discuss the latest in energy generation, distribution and conservation. Their guests range from academics and climate change activists to gadget designers, scientists and consumers. Why not tune into the TWiEpodcast at www.thisweekinenergy.tv?

littleCollie also produces the Saturday edition of the EVcast, a three-times-a-week show about plug-in Vehicles. Why not drop in on the EVcast team at www.evcast.com?

If you're an iPhone user then don't forget to keep your eyes open for our latest creation hitting Apple's App Store in 2010. EVtracker helps you keep accurate records about your EV's efficiency and battery health! Best of all, it's FREE!

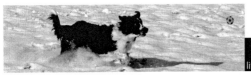

Productions. Apps. Consulting
We keep our eye on the ball.

littleCollie.com

To discuss our shows, or contact us about consulting in podcasting, programming or green tech, head over to www.littlecollie.com

Breinigsville, PA USA
19 December 2010
251805BV00001B/1-2/P